INTRODUCTION

Every year thousands of holidaymakers flock to the coast. Most of these are city-dwellers, and the chance to enjoy fresh unpolluted air and wide seascapes is one of the great attractions of a seaside break. Of course, many people will spend most of their holiday sunbathing on some crowded beach, and that is all they ask. For many others, the coast offers the chance to explore a whole new and exciting world. Children especially are very fond of poking around among the mysterious pools of water exposed at low tide on a rocky coast, and the discovery of a single crab can cause great excitement. The casual holiday pastime of 'rock pooling' is becoming increasingly popular, and this book aims to increase the pleasure derived from this pursuit by enabling most of what is discovered to be identified.

The life of the seashore, especially where rocks abound, is far more diverse than in even the richest habitats on land, and it is this opportunity to meet up with some very strange and exotic organisms that lends added zest to any kind of nature exploration on the coast. Whole groups of animals are purely found in salt water. These include all the members of the phylum Echinodermata (starfish, brittle-stars, sea urchins and sea cucumbers), all the sea squirts in the class Ascidiacea and the overwhelming majority of jellyfish, as well as all the corals and sea anemones in the phylum Cnidaria. The variety of molluscs and worms is also generally greater than in most terrestrial habitats, and molluscs such as periwinkles, limpets and mussels can occur in enormous abundance. On land the crustaceans are represented mainly by a few woodlice, but in the sea this great group reaches its peak of diversity, with a huge variety of crabs, shrimps, isopods and the strange un-crustacean-like barnacles all being found in large numbers and considerable variety on the shore. Among plants, the algae, which on land are mainly represented as inconspicuous green or orange crusts, form a broad and very hard-to-miss fringe of seaweeds between the sea and the land, often being locally dominant on most rocky shores and occurring in a huge diversity of shapes and colours, frequently reaching a considerable size and complexity.

The species in this book have been chosen because they are present on most shores and are the species most likely to be found by the average person engaging in a spot of casual rock pooling. The majority are found mainly or solely on rocky shores as this is where the process of discovering what is present is fairly easy and the variety is very great. A selection of species from sandy or muddy shores is also included. Muddy shores can be unpleasant to work on but can be rewarding for the spectacular displays of flowers such as sea lavenders. Sandy shores are a favourite for families at play, but most of the superabundance of life present is found within the sand, so is not normally on view. Cliffs often form the backdrop to a rocky shore, so you may get a glimpse of the cliff-top fauna and flora as you make your way down to the shore, or take a walk along a cliff-top path. Cliff-top grasslands can have a wealth of wildflowers humming with insect life, so it has been necessary to restrict the coverage here mainly to purely coastal plants, excluding the many species that are also common inland. The same applies to sand dunes, which are very attractive habitats, often carpeted with exciting wild-flowers such as orchids. However, as many of these are also found inland, only the plants restricted to sand dunes or sandy beach tops have been included here. The insects chosen are also mainly or exclusively coastal. Few birds are included because these are described in a separate volume in this series, as well as in many other books. This allows more space for the organisms that form the nucleus of this book: the plants and animals revealed when the ebbing tide uncovers the exciting world of the rocky shore.

HOW TO USE THIS BOOK

For each of the main entries there is a colour **photograph** showing the most distinctive features of the particular organism. Each species has been photographed in its natural habitat where you are likely to find it, giving you an idea of how it will appear against its normal background. This is especially important for many of the rock pool animals, where photographs taken in indoor aquaria can give an extremely misleading impression that the organism is very easy to see.

The accompanying **text** gives background information about the organism featured, including advice on where it may be found within Europe, and general hints about how to identify it, as well as details on its biology. The **ID Fact File** gives more precise details about the key features of the organism. This normally includes information about the time of year when it may be seen. As most seashore organisms are present throughout the year, information on season is only given where this is relevant, for example for species that die back in winter or migrate into deeper water. Some south-western coasts are much warmer than those in the north, so the dates given may fluctuate from place to place and from year to year, being also affected by the weather.

For the complete beginner the easiest way to use this book is to scan through the pictures until you come upon one that resembles what you have found. As expertise increases, you will be able to go straight to the correct section, reducing your search considerably. There are often several species that look very similar, with only one being illustrated, so if your discovery does not quite fit the picture and the description, check the ID Fact File for details of the lookalikes. All the really common animals are included here, as are many of the larger and more abundant seaweeds, but this is a large and difficult group, which can perplex even the experienced biologist. Many common species are not included, either because they are unattractive or because identification presents too many problems.

The different types of shore organisms are identified by a **symbol** at the top of the page, as an aid to narrowing down the possibilities more rapidly. The symbols used and organisms to which they refer are as follows, in order of sequence within the following pages:

Algae (seaweeds)

Lichens

Vascular plants (flowering plants and ferns)

Sponges

Cnidarians (jellyfish, hydroids, sea anemones)

Worms

Crustaceans (barnacles, crabs, shrimps etc.)

Spiders, Pycnogonids (sea spiders)

Insects

Molluscs

Echinoderms (starfish, sea urchins, sea cucumbers)

Sea Squirts

Fish

Birds

FINDING SEASHORE LIFE

To make the best of your time on the seashore a little advance planning is wise. If you arrive at the wrong time you will see very little. It is common to see families, complete with excited children laden down with buckets and nets, arrive at the shore for an enjoyable bout of 'rock pooling' just as the tide is coming in and covering the whole shore with water. To avoid such disappointment it is best to acquire a set of local tide tables. These can be bought in local stationers and other shops and will give the times of lowest and highest tides (two of each, every 24 hours) in the local area, usually on a county basis. If you go somewhere else, you will need another set of local tables, as the tides vary greatly from one area to another. For example in Cornwall the lowest tides, when more of the shore will be uncovered than at any other time, normally occur around the middle of the day, which is perfect for most people. By contrast, further north these low tides often occur at very inconvenient times, early in the morning or late at night. The lowest tides, known as spring tides, occur from February to April and September to October. March and April sometimes see tides that drop even below the 'normal' low water mark, adding a real 'buzz' to any visit as many creatures that are normally covered with water will be revealed for a short period. Bear in mind that the converse of an exceptionally low tide will be an exceptionally high one when it comes back in, covering parts of the shore that usually remain dry for weeks at a time.

Not all rocky shores will be worth exploring. Soft rocks such as chalk and shales are too easily eroded for much life to become established. Where the shore lies very exposed to northerly gales, as on the north coast of Devon and Cornwall, much of the rock will be devoid of life, as organisms will be forced to hide in crevices and gulleys to escape the force of the waves. On such exposed coasts sheltered bays will be the best places to visit, but will still be inferior to sheltered coasts facing south, which can be absolutely teeming with living organisms. It is best to arrive just as the tide is beginning to recede, when you can follow it down. Arriving on an incoming tide will cause you to rush, especially as the best (lowermost) zone of the shore quickly becomes inundated with water.

On the upper shore many creatures such as barnacles and periwinkles occur in large numbers and are very conspicuous. On the middle and lower shores, progressively yielding up their treasures as the tide ebbs, you will have to search more intensively to discover the real gems. Looking in rock pools will reveal many different seaweeds, as well as various sea anemones, usually accompanied by shrimps and sometimes also by sea slugs. Lower down the shore the best procedure is to look beneath the larger stones. Take care not to hurt yourself when lifting these, and try to work in pairs. As one lifts the rock, the other can check underneath for crabs and other creatures clinging to the underside or left behind on the ground beneath. The majority of the seashore animals illustrated in this book were found beneath stones in this way. Unfortunately many crabs and fishes will immediately try to take cover beneath the lowermost edge of the uplifted rock, and these can easily be squashed and killed when you replace the (often very heavy) stone. This is where a second person can help out by netting the creature or persuading it to move to safety with the aid of a stick. The rock can then be **eased gently** back into position, taking great care not to crush the sea anemones, crabs, starfish and other creatures that will often still be clinging to its underside. If possible, try and replace the stone so that a slight gap is left beneath. Remember, you are intruding upon the private world of these creatures, some of which may be rare, and their lives are in your hands. **Always** replace a stone that you have turned up, as most of its inhabitants will die if you turn it over and leave it. Also, if you temporarily remove your discoveries to a bucket for closer inspection, try and replace them in the same area of the shore as you found them. In particular, creatures from the lower shore will not survive for long if replaced in a pool on the upper shore.

SAFETY WARNING

The seashore is a hazardous place and at all times you need to be aware of the risks. The following points should be borne in mind:

1) Be constantly aware of the state of the tide, and do not wander off onto parts of the shore where you will be cut off when the tide comes back in.

2) Do not wander out onto sticky mud in estuaries; you may become trapped and unable to retreat before the incoming tide overwhelms you.

3) Do not walk too near cliff edges, or sit below crumbly-looking cliffs. Falls of rock are frequent and unpredictable.

4) Wear non-slip footwear. Bare feet have good grip, but can be cut by the sharp shells of barnacles.

5) Be careful when walking over rocks. Those covered in seaweeds (particularly bright green slimy-looking ones) can be lethally slippery. Many rocks also tilt unexpectedly when they take your weight. In particular, do not refer to this book while walking over rocks.

The size measurements given in this book are the largest and smallest recorded at the time of going to print. Some variations with older publications may therefore be found.

ALGAE

Gutweed
Enteromorpha intestinalis

ID FACT FILE

TYPE:
Green

SIZE:
Up to 75 cm long

DESCRIPTION:
Fronds simple,
bright grass-
green, tubular,
rather inflated,
arising from a
minute disc-like
base and with a
randomly spaced
string of
constrictions
giving the
appearance of
a series of
bladders

HABITAT:
Upper shore only

LOOKALIKES:
There are
several similar-
looking species.
The fronds of
E. compressa are
distinctively
branched. In
E. linza the
fronds are
smaller, more
flattened and
with a spiral
appearance

Because it occurs near the top of the shore,
large patches of this bright green seaweed are
often exposed for long periods, forming a slimy
carpet over the rocks as soon as the tide begins
to drop. Anyone familiar with this plant will
tread very carefully across such a carpet as the
fronds of Gutweed are notoriously slippery and
can easily cause a nasty fall. The fronds lying
coiled on the rocks resemble an animal's gut,
hence the common name. The walls are only
one cell thick. Gutweed is very common on the
upper shore, especially where a freshwater
stream runs across it, or in pools diluted by
rainwater. It is cosmopolitan.

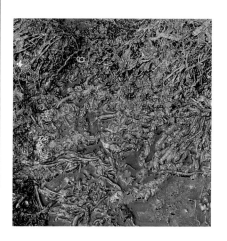

ALGAE

Sea Lettuce
Ulva lactuca

J	F	M	A	M	J
J	A	S	O	N	D

ID FACT FILE

TYPE:
Green

SIZE:
Frond 10–30 cm across

DESCRIPTION:
Frond light to bright green, rather crumpled-looking, broad and membranous, with a wavy margin like a rather delicate lettuce leaf, developing from a tiny disc-like base

HABITAT:
At all levels on the shore

LOOKALIKES:
Monostroma grevillei is a very similar but more delicate and translucent plant with a more funnel-shaped frond. It grows only in lower shore rock pools, never on the upper shore as in Sea Lettuce

Sea Lettuce often forms a crumpled green and very slippery carpet across rocks on the upper shore when the tide is out. It also makes beautiful swaying forests of broad green fronds in middle shore rock pools and on the lower shore, where it is only exposed by the lowest spring tides. When out of water the fronds collapse into a limp and unattractive state. The fronds become edged with white once the sexual products have been released, and may also become ragged with wear and tear. Like Gutweed, *Enteromorpha intestinalis*, see opposite, Sea Lettuce is often found in brackish conditions where fresh water is present. Distribution is worldwide. Sometimes eaten, being called 'Green Laver'.

ALGAE

Velvet Horn

Codium tomentosum

ID FACT FILE

TYPE:
Green

SIZE:
Fronds to 30 cm
long, about
5 mm in
diameter

DESCRIPTION:
Fronds a
beautiful dark
velvety green,
cylindrical or very
faintly flattened,
branching freely
in a regular
fashion and
eventually
terminating in a
dense crown of
short branchlets

HABITAT:
In rock pools on
the middle and
lower shore

LOOKALIKES:
C. fragile is
larger and
spreads further
to the north

Velvet Horn is a very distinctive although often
rather scarce seaweed which must be looked
for in deep rock pools on the middle and lower
shore. Even when present, only a few plants
are often all that can be found. The cylindrical
and rather spongy stems have a fascinatingly
felt-like texture and are normally very dark
green, not usually turning paler when exposed
to bright sunlight. The holdfast is usually
attached to rocks immersed in sand or mud.
Distribution is restricted to southwest Britain
and the Atlantic and Mediterranean coasts
of Europe.

ALGAE

Jelly Buttons
Leathesia difformis

J	F	M	A	M	J
J	A	S	O	N	D

ID FACT FILE

TYPE:
Brown

SIZE:
2–5 cm across

DESCRIPTION:
A bulbous,
yellowish-brown,
glossy mass
resembling a
blob of jelly or oil
rather than a
plant. The plants
are solid at first,
soon becoming
hollow

HABITAT:
On the middle
and lower shore

LOOKALIKES:
The Oyster Thief,
*Colpomenia
peregrina* is
similar but often
larger, and has
thinner walls
which are
covered in large
numbers of tiny
dark dots.
Codium bursa is
a solid dark
green mass

Jelly Buttons is an aptly named plant, for
smaller plants in particular resemble rather
flattened blobs of jelly. They are revealed by
the ebbing tide, scattered around on rocks
and seaweeds on the middle and lower shores,
usually just above the Oarweed zone. The
younger plants are solid, but gradually become
inflated as they grow larger, so that they
eventually become quite broad and hollow.
This is a common plant around the North Sea,
Channel and Atlantic coasts of Europe.

J	F	M	A	M	J
J	A	S	O	N	D

Oarweed
Laminaria digitata

ID FACT FILE

TYPE:
Brown

SIZE:
Frond to 2 m or longer, 60–80 cm across

DESCRIPTION:
Frond dark blackish yellow, shiny, flattened, arising from a very flexible, smooth and cylindrical stem connected to a large, branching holdfast attached to rock

HABITAT:
Lower shore and below

LOOKALIKES:
Cuvie, *L. hyperborea* is very similar but with a roughened stem. In Furbelows, *Saccorhiza polyschides*, see page 16, the stem is flat, with a sinuous edge

Also often known as Tangle, this and the following two species belong to a group of very large seaweeds known as kelps, which usually form a broad and very prominent band on the lower shore, only becoming fully exposed on the lowest spring tides. In Oarweed the stem is smooth and cylindrical, and the broad frond is shaped rather like a flat hand with numerous strap-like fingers. When exposed by low tides the fronds sprawl over the rocks, whereas in the similar but rough-stemmed Cuvie they remain upright.

ALGAE

Sea Belt
Laminaria saccharina

| J | F | M | A | M | J |
| J | A | S | O | N | D |

ID FACT FILE

TYPE:
Brown

SIZE:
Frond to 4 m
long, 12–15 cm
broad

DESCRIPTION:
Frond long,
unbranched,
belt-like with a
ruffled surface
and wavy edges,
yellowish-brown
at first, becoming
dark blackish-
brown. Stem
smooth, slender,
arising from a
branched
holdfast

HABITAT:
Lower shore

LOOKALIKES:
Dabberlocks,
Alaria esculenta
is shorter,
greener, with a
prominent midrib
running up the
frond

With its long, rather narrow, unbranched
fronds Sea Belt is the easiest of the kelps to
recognise. It is often abundant on the lower
shore where it can only be observed on the
lowest tides, but at other times it may be
spotted more easily in deep, permanent pools
on the middle shore. The brittle dried fronds
are often used to forecast rain, becoming soft
and limp when rain approaches, hence the
alternative name of 'Poor Man's Weatherglass',
which is often used for this common plant.
Abundant around the coasts of Europe.

ALGAE

| J | F | M | A | M | J |
| J | A | S | O | N | D |

Furbelows
Saccorhiza polyschides

ID FACT FILE

TYPE:
Brown

SIZE:
Frond up to
4.5 m long

DESCRIPTION:
Hand-like frond
with strap-like
'fingers',
resembles
Oarweed but is
paler yellowish-
brown and stem
is quite different,
being flattened
and with a very
wavy margin

HABITAT:
Lowest part of
the shore

SEASON:
An annual,
present only in
summer

LOOKALIKES:
Oarweed,
*Laminaria
digitata*, page
14, has smooth,
cylindrical stem
(rough stem in
Cuvie, *L.
hyperborea*)

Although it is placed in a different genus,
Furbelows closely resembles Oarweed,
Laminaria digitata, see page 14, and is another
of the kelps. Unlike the other kelps, Furbelows
is an annual, dying off in autumn. In the
following spring young plants grow so rapidly
that by late summer they have attained the
greatest bulk of any European seaweed.
The holdfast of this species is unique, being
shaped like a rather flattened, inverted
basket with a very warty surface. Furbelows
is common around the North Sea, Channel
and Atlantic coasts.

ALGAE

| J | F | M | A | M | J |
| J | A | S | O | N | D |

Thongweed
Himanthalia elongata

ID FACT FILE

TYPE:
Brown

SIZE:
Main plant 3 cm across, with reproductive bodies up to 3 m long

DESCRIPTION:
Main plant resembling rather concave, short-stalked brownish-yellow mushroom, from which long slender thong-like, sparingly branched reproductive bodies arise in summer

HABITAT:
Lower shore

LOOKALIKES:
Mermaid's Tresses or Dead Men's Ropes, *Chorda filum* is even longer, unbranched, has no disc-like perennial stage and occurs in deeper estuarine waters

Thongweed can be a bit of a puzzle as it occurs in two quite dissimilar-looking stages. The button-like perennial stage is often attached in large numbers to rocks on the lower shore and is visible throughout the year. From spring onwards the long, once- or twice-branched reproductive bodies arise from the centre of the 'button', often densely draping the rocks like dreadlocks when stranded by a spring tide. In autumn these rot and break off, leaving a short stump. Common around the North Sea, Channel and Atlantic coasts.

ALGAE

J	F	M	A	M	J
J	A	S	O	N	D

Japweed
Sargassum muticum

ID FACT FILE

TYPE:
Brown

SIZE:
Frond to 1 m
long or more

DESCRIPTION:
Stem narrow,
cylindrical, with
branches
occurring at
regular intervals
on alternate
sides up its
length. Colour
yellowish-brown

HABITAT:
In pools all up
the shore and in
estuaries

LOOKALIKES:
Sea Oak,
*Halidrys
siliquosa*, page
26, is shorter,
sturdier with
many elongated
pod-like gas
bladders

This seaweed is a relatively recent and very unwelcome newcomer to European shores, having been accidentally introduced from the eastern Pacific region on oysters. In many places, especially in Cornwall and other parts of southwest England, rock pools on the middle shore are now swamped by dense forests of this plant, at the expense of more attractive native seaweeds such as Tamarisk Weed, *Cystoseira tamariscifolia*, see page 25. Such native seaweeds also support a diverse array of small animal life, which does not thrive on the invasive alien.

ALGAE

Knotted Wrack
Ascophyllum nodosum

J	F	M	A	M	J
J	A	S	O	N	D

ID FACT FILE

TYPE:
Brown

SIZE:
Frond to 1 m
long

DESCRIPTION:
Frond yellowish-
brown to olive-
green, narrow,
flattened, lacking
a midrib,
sparingly
branched,
interrupted at
intervals by
large, soft egg-
like bladders
filled with gas

HABITAT:
Middle shore

LOOKALIKES:
Bladder Wrack,
*Fucus
vesiculosus*, see
page 22, has
more numerous,
much smaller
bladders on far
broader, strap-
like fronds

Also known as Egg Wrack, this is one of a
number of common species called wracks in
the family Fucaceae. On the middle zone of
most shores Knotted Wrack forms a dense
carpet, which excludes most other seaweeds
except for a red seaweed *Polysiphonia lanosa*,
which grows as an epiphyte on the fronds of
the Knotted Wrack. The large egg-like bladders set at intervals along the fronds enable
Knotted Wrack to float upright at high tide,
seeking as much light as possible.

ALGAE

| J | F | M | A | M | J |
| J | A | S | O | N | D |

Channelled Wrack
Pelvetia canaliculata

ID FACT FILE

TYPE:
Brown

SIZE:
Frond to 15 cm
long, 4–5 mm
across

DESCRIPTION:
Fronds without
midrib, with
incurved margin
forming a
channel, no
bladders, forked
tips to fronds
formed by
swollen elongate-
ovoid roughened
reproductive
bodies

HABITAT:
Uppermost part
of shore

LOOKALIKES:
Small forms of
the common
Fucus species
have midrib to
stem; Knotted
Wrack,
*Ascophyllum
nodosum*, see
page 19, has
large bladders.
See also Spiral
Wrack, *F. spiralis*,
opposite;
Horned Wrack,
F. ceranoides,
page 23

Channelled Wrack forms dense tufts covering
the rocks at the uppermost part of the shore,
extending down the shore into the upper limit
of the zone occupied by Spiral Wrack, *Fucus
spiralis*, see opposite. Living so high on the
shore, during periods of neap tides Channelled
Wrack may be left exposed for days on end,
and in hot summer weather it becomes very
shrivelled and crisped, turning almost black.
Normally the concave section of the stems lies
against the rocks, conserving at least some
water until the tide returns. Tiny, undersized
plants can survive above the high tide level,
relying solely on salty spray.

| J | F | M | A | M | J |
| J | A | S | O | N | D |

Spiral or Flat Wrack
Fucus spiralis

ID FACT FILE

TYPE:
Brown

SIZE:
Frond up to
30 cm long,
about 15 mm
broad

DESCRIPTION:
Frond yellowish-
brown, flattened,
often rather
twisted, divided
several times
into strap-like
segments, with a
prominent midrib
and oval, warty
reproductive
bodies at the
tips

HABITAT:
Upper shore

LOOKALIKES:
Channelled
Wrack, *Pelvetia
caniculata*, see
opposite, is
smaller and has
a channelled
stem and no
midrib

Spiral Wrack grows as a distinct band on the upper shore, below the level normally occupied by Channelled Wrack, *Pelvetia canaliculata*, see opposite, and above the next zone down, occupied by Bladder Wrack, *Fucus vesiculosus*, see page 22, and Knotted Wrack, *Ascophyllum nodosum*, see page 19. On gently sloping shores each of these zones is quite broad and discrete, but on steeply sloping shores, e.g. on parts of the river Fal in Cornwall, the zones are very narrow and squashed into one another. Spiral Wrack is common and widely distributed around most European coasts.

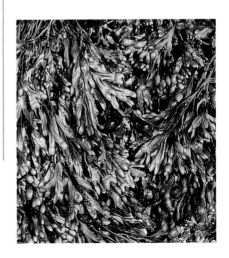

ALGAE

J	F	M	A	M	J
J	A	S	O	N	D

Bladder Wrack
Fucus vesiculosus

ID FACT FILE

Type:
Brown

Size:
Frond up to 1 m
long, to 5 cm
broad

Description:
Fronds greenish-
yellow to dark
olive-brown,
flattened, with
prominent
midrib, smooth.
Pea-sized
bladders occur at
intervals, tips of
frond with forked
oval reproductive
bodies

Habitat:
Middle shore

Lookalikes:
Bladderless
forms occur
and could be
confused with
Toothed Wrack,
Fucus serratus,
see page 24,
but this has
strongly toothed
margins. See
also Knotted
Wrack,
*Ascophyllum
nodosum*,
page 19

Bladder Wrack is very variable and becomes
even more confusing when it forms hybrids
with other wracks. In its typical and most
common form it is easily recognised by the
numerous smooth air-filled bladders, about the
size of large peas, which children love to pop,
and can be quite noisy when trodden
underfoot, hence the alternative name of
Popweed. The bladders act as floats, lifting the
plant as the tide comes in. Plants growing on
very exposed shores often lack bladders.
Bladder Wrack is common on rocky shores
throughout northern Europe.

ALGAE

Horned Wrack
Fucus ceranoides

J	F	M	A	M	J
J	A	S	O	N	D

ID FACT FILE

TYPE:
Brown

SIZE:
Frond to 90 cm
long

DESCRIPTION:
Fronds pale
greenish-olive,
relatively small,
branching, with
narrow midrib,
margins entire,
neither toothed
nor folded
inwards,
sometimes
slightly undulate.
Fruiting branches
narrow, in fan-like
arrangement at
tips of fronds

HABITAT:
On rocks in
estuaries

LOOKALIKES:
Channelled
Wrack, *Pelvetia
canaliculata* is
also small but
has no midrib

Horned Wrack is most easily recognised from
the situation in which it grows. It is not found
as part of the zonation that the other wracks
form on rocky shores, but occurs on the rocky
edges of estuaries where the seawater is
diluted by considerable quantities of freshwater. Here Horned Wrack will carpet the
rocks to the exclusion of all else. The pointed,
horn-like reproductive receptacles form a
characteristic fan-like arrangement that also
contributes towards recognition of this species
which is found widely around the Atlantic,
Channel and North Sea coasts of Europe.

ALGAE

| J | F | M | A | M | J |
| J | A | S | O | N | D |

ID FACT FILE

TYPE:
Brown

SIZE:
Frond to 60 cm
long, 2.5 cm
wide

DESCRIPTION:
Fronds dark
olive-brown,
blackish when
wet, flat,
strap-like,
repeatedly
branching.
Margins with
irregular
arrangement of
sharp, forward-
directed teeth.
Midrib rather
thick and
conspicuous

HABITAT:
Lower shore

LOOKALIKES:
Other wracks
lack toothed
margins and
have other major
differences

Toothed Wrack
Fucus serratus

Toothed Wrack occurs lower down the shore than any of the other wracks, forming dense gleaming carpets which sprawl across the rocks at the low tide mark, just above the start of the kelp zone. Great care is needed when moving around in the Toothed Wrack zone, as this species is far more slippery when wet than any of the other wracks. Male and female plants are separate, and the female reproductive receptacles are very inconspicuous, being merely slightly thickened patches near the tips of the fronds. Toothed Wrack is very common around the coasts of Northern Europe.

ALGAE

Tamarisk Weed
Cystoseira tamariscifolia

J	F	M	A	M	J
J	A	S	O	N	D

ID FACT FILE

TYPE:
Brown

SIZE:
Frond to 45 cm
long

DESCRIPTION:
Plants forming a
dense, many-
branched olive-
brown bush,
covered with
short spines
and usually
with a green
iridescence when
under water. Gas
bladders small,
oval

HABITAT:
In rock pools on
the lower shore

LOOKALIKES:
C. fibrosa is not
iridescent and
has much larger,
conspicuous
bladders

A large rock pool on the lower shore filled
with an iridescent bluish-green forest of this
beautiful seaweed is one of the most striking
sights to be found on the shores of northern
Europe. Although the green iridescence is
generally present, it is sometimes absent from
individual plants, which are then just plain
brown. The iridescence also usually disappears
when the plant is out of the water. The entire
frond is covered with short (4 mm long) spines
that are often called leaves. This superb
seaweed is rather local, being restricted to the
coasts of southwest Britain and the Atlantic
coast of mainland Europe, southward to the
Mediterranean.

ALGAE

J	F	M	A	M	J
J	A	S	O	N	D

Sea Oak

Halidrys siliquosa

ID FACT FILE

TYPE:
Brown

SIZE:
Frond to 1 m
long

DESCRIPTION:
Forming a sturdy,
rather flattened
but shapely
brownish-green
bush. Main stem
giving rise to
side branches
which alternate
in a characteris-
tic zigzag
fashion. Gas
bladders
resemble long
seed pods

HABITAT:
In pools on the
lower shore

LOOKALIKES:
Japweed,
*Sargassum
muticum*, page
18, is of similar
colour but lacks
elongated
bladders

The common name for this plant is not
particularly apt as in no respect does it
resemble an Oak. Its most conspicuous and
distinctive feature is the presence of long,
slender bladders at the tips of the side
branches. These bladders, which can be up to
5 cm long and 4 mm broad, resemble the
seed pods of various plants in the cabbage
family. Each bladder is divided into several
internal compartments whose walls are visible
at the surface by transverse bands, giving
the bladder a rather ribbed appearance.
Sea Oak is fairly common around the coasts
of northern Europe.

ALGAE

Forked Rubberweed
Bifurcaria bifurcata

J	F	M	A	M	J
J	A	S	O	N	D

ID FACT FILE

TYPE:
Brown

SIZE:
Frond to 30 cm long

DESCRIPTION:
Fronds smooth, rubbery, tough, yellowish-olive, forming clumps of cylindrical, bootlace-like stems which from about halfway up begin to form branches which then again branch one or more times. Branch-tips fairly blunt

HABITAT:
Pools on middle and lower shore

LOOKALIKES:
Furcellaria lumbricalis, a red seaweed, is stiffer, with its branching bifid, and with pointed tips

The vertical margins of rock pools on the middle and lower shore may be obscured by a dense fringe of this plant, which grows out at right angles to the rock and lies horizontally in the water. It is extremely tough and rubbery, making it difficult to detach from the rock. The plant persists throughout the year, and from April to October the terminal parts of the branches may bear slightly swollen, blunt-tipped reproductive organs some 3–4 cm long. Distribution is southerly, restricted to the southwesterly coasts of England, Wales and Ireland, and the Atlantic coasts of Europe.

ALGAE

J	F	M	A	M	J
J	A	S	O	N	D

Red Rags
Dilsea carnosa

ID FACT FILE

TYPE:
Red

SIZE:
Frond to 40 cm
long, 12 cm
broad

DESCRIPTION:
Fronds tufted,
smooth and
shiny, dark blood-
red, leathery,
flattened,
unbranched
beyond the short
cylindrical stem
which grows from
a disc holdfast
attached to rock

HABITAT:
Lowermost part
of the shore, on
rocks

LOOKALIKES:
*Callblepharis
ciliata* is paler
red and has
numerous short
branchlets
around its
margins.
Also see Dulse,
*Palmaria
palmata*, page
35; *Callophyllis
laciniata*,
page 42

This is one of the larger of our red seaweeds
and is easily recognised from its dark red
coloration and the unbranched shape of the
frond, which is highly succulent with a
noticeably gelatinous texture. Older adult
specimens tend to become split and rather
ragged near the top (hence the common
name), altering the appearance somewhat,
although the original shape remains evident.
This is a perennial seaweed found throughout
the year. Young plants become established in
autumn and grow to maturity throughout the
winter. The only chance of finding this plant
is to visit the shore during low spring tides.
Red Rags is common on most coasts of
northern Europe.

ALGAE

Coralweed
Corallina officinalis

| J | F | M | A | M | J |
| J | A | S | O | N | D |

ID FACT FILE

TYPE:
Red

SIZE:
Frond to 12 cm
long

DESCRIPTION:
Fronds usually
pinkish, rigid,
hard and brittle,
composed of
numerous short
bead-like
segments linked
together to form
a chain; frond
branching and
fan-like towards
the tips

HABITAT:
Rock pools on
middle shore and
on lower shore

LOOKALIKES:
Jania rubens,
page 30, is deep-
er pink, forming
very dense tufts
with thread-like
segments.
Also see
Necklaceweed,
*Lomentaria
articulata*
page 34

This is probably the most characteristic
seaweed found in rock pools on the middle
shore, in which it often forms a dense fringe.
Although most often a rather dull pink,
Coralweed can also be tinged with yellow,
mauve or dull purple. The whole plant is
rather stiff and brittle as it is impregnated with
lime and magnesium, and only the joints are
uncalcified, leading to some degree of
flexibility. Coralweed prefers shallow pools
in which it is often dominant. It is found
abundantly on all rocky European coasts.

ALGAE

A Red Seaweed
Jania rubens

ID FACT FILE

TYPE:
Red

SIZE:
2.5–10 cm long

DESCRIPTION:
A tufted,
multi-branched
species of a
beautiful
rosy-purplish
shade,
deepening as the
summer wears
on. Urn-shaped
female
receptacles
occur in the forks
of the branches

HABITAT:
In pools on the
lower shore

LOOKALIKES:
*Cystoclonium
purpureum* is
less rigid and
has globular
receptacles near
the tips of the
branchlets. See
also Coralweed,
*Corallina
officinalis*,
page 29

This is one of the prettiest seaweeds found on European coasts, where it is abundant in the south, becoming rarer northwards and scarce around the North Sea. In springtime the young growth is ball-like, but the degree of branching gradually increases until quite large spreading plants are formed. These are usually attached to other seaweeds, often in huge quantity in sheltered bays, although this species is also present on quite exposed coasts. The plant is quite stiff to the touch, but not nearly as rigid as the closely related Coralweed, *Corallina officinalis*, see page 29.

ALGAE

Shellweed
Mesophyllum lichenoides

J	F	M	A	M	J
J	A	S	O	N	D

ID FACT FILE

TYPE:
Red

SIZE:
To 1.5 cm across

DESCRIPTION:
Fronds hard,
shell-like, only
1 mm thick, pale
pink or buff, with
darker concentric
banding

HABITAT:
In rock pools on
middle and lower
shore

LOOKALIKES:
None

This distinctive little seaweed resembles
numerous flattened shells, and attaches
itself to other seaweeds, usually to Coralweed,
Corallina officinalis, see page 29. As in that
species, Shellweed is one of the so-called
calcareous seaweeds in which a considerable
proportion of lime is incorporated into the
plant, making it hard and quite brittle.
Although absent from many shores, Shellweed
is widespread and can be abundant where
found, often being very conspicuous on the
dense growth of Coralweed that is typical of the
shallow margins of pools on the middle shore.

ALGAE

J	F	M	A	M	J
J	A	S	O	N	D

Red Encrusting Alga

Lithophyllum incrustans

ID FACT FILE

TYPE:
Red

SIZE:
2–20 mm thick

DESCRIPTION:
Calcareous alga forming a pink or purplish sheet across rocks, forming more or less circular lobes or patches with uniformly coloured margins. Surface rather knobbly

HABITAT:
Middle shore downwards

LOOKALIKES:
Lithothamnion lenormandi is a more attractive reddish-violet and has a pale margin to the lobes

Few people realise that the broad sheets of bright pink, enamel-like growths, which cover the bottoms of rock pools and undersides of rocks on most shores are actually living plants. Like Coralweed, *Corallina officinalis*, see page 29, these are calcareous algae formed solely of a simple solid crust up to 2 cm thick. Where the crusts overlap they form ridges. In the very similar but more deeply pigmented *Lithothamnion lenormandi* the crusts are much thinner and are marked with concentric rings. Both species are very common around all European coasts.

ALGAE

J	F	M	A	M	J
J	A	S	O	N	D

ID FACT FILE

TYPE:
Red

SIZE:
To 20 cm long

DESCRIPTION:
Fronds dark
purplish-red or
blackish,
cylindrical,
dividing regularly
and with forked
tips which taper
to a point or are
thickened if
reproductive
bodies are
present. Holdfast
is a mass of
'rootlets'

HABITAT:
In pools on
middle and
lower shore

LOOKALIKES:
*Polyides
rotundus* is very
similar but its
holdfast is a
fleshy disc

Wormweed
Furcellaria lumbricalis

This species is widespread around European coastlines and is characteristic of pools on rocky shores where it can be abundant. Although the slender fronds usually taper gradually to a point, in asexual plants the branches are tipped by much plumper spindle-shaped pod-like growths some 3 cm long and about 3 mm in diameter at the broadest point. Male and female plants are separate, with the former having yellowish-pink ovoid tips to the fronds. As in many 'reds', plants exposed to strong sunlight turn greenish-yellow.

ALGAE

J	F	M	A	M	J
J	A	S	O	N	D

Necklaceweed
Lomentaria articulata

ID FACT FILE

TYPE:
Red

SIZE:
Frond up to
12 cm long

DESCRIPTION:
Plant tufted, pale
to deep crimson
(greenish in
brightly lit
situations).
Fronds with
constrictions at
regular intervals,
like string of
beads, with
branches
arising from
constrictions

HABITAT:
On rocks on
lower shore

LOOKALIKES:
*Griffithsia
corallinoides*,
also has stem
divided into
beads, but these
taper from top to
bottom; see
also Coralweed,
*Corallina
officinalis*,
page 29

Although the normal colour for this seaweed is
a deep crimson, in shallower water paler red
forms are found, and in very brightly lit
situations all the red pigment is lost and the
plants are a bright yellowish-green. All colour
forms may be found side by side and even
grading into one another on a single plant. The
bead-like structure of the stems is particularly
obvious in the greenish forms, which glisten
brightly when exposed to sunlight.
Necklaceweed often carpets the rocks locally
towards the lower part of the shore, and is
found around the shores of northwest Europe.

ALGAE

Dulse
Palmaria palmata

J	F	M	A	M	J
J	A	S	O	N	D

ID FACT FILE

TYPE:
Red

SIZE:
Frond up to
30 cm long

DESCRIPTION:
A tufted,
multi-branched
species of a
beautiful
rosy-purplish
shade,
deepening as the
summer wears
on. Urn-shaped
female
receptacles
occur in the forks
of the branches

HABITAT:
On rocks on the
lower shore

LOOKALIKES:
See Red Rags,
Dilsea carnosa,
page 28, and
*Callophyllis
laciniata*,
page 42

Dulse is one of the largest of the red seaweeds found on the shore and is often abundant on rocks just above the kelp zone, as well as attached to the kelps themselves, particularly Cuvie, *Laminaria hyperborea*. Although the shape of the frond in Dulse is very variable, it is a plant that will quickly become easily recognised. It is the best-known of the edible seaweeds, although the fronds are rather tough and taste mostly of salt. Sheep seem rather fond of it when there is little else available. Dulse is found abundantly around all the northern European coasts.

ALGAE

| J | F | M | A | M | J |
| J | A | S | O | N | D |

Crimson Featherweed
Heterosiphonia plumosa

ID FACT FILE

TYPE:
Red

SIZE:
Frond to about
20 cm long

DESCRIPTION:
Fronds a
beautiful deep
crimson,
flattened,
profusely
branching all in
one plane,
primary branches
arising
alternately but
not at regular
intervals,
secondary
branches also
subdividing

HABITAT:
Lower shore

LOOKALIKES:
There are
numerous other
small red
seaweeds but
none as
flattened and
attractive as
this one

Crimson Featherweed is probably the most attractive of the smaller, profusely branching red seaweeds likely to be found between tidemarks. Unlike most of the others, it does not immediately collapse into a shapeless mass when taken out of the water, but retains its elegant feathery shape. The crimson shade is particularly striking and the fronds are noticeably flattened and will be found attached to rocks or other larger seaweeds on the lower shore. Widespread in northern Europe.

ALGAE

J	F	M	A	M	J
J	A	S	O	N	D

Pepper Dulse
Laurencia pinnatifida

ID FACT FILE

Type:
Red

Size:
Frond up to
about 7 cm long
on lower shore,
only about 2 cm
on mid-shore

Description:
Fronds flattened
on lower shore,
more tufted and
fern-like on
exposed rocks
on middle shore.
Stems with
alternate
branches, these
sub-dividing into
short stubby
branchlets.
Colour brownish-
purple on lower
shore, brownish-
yellow in well-lit
zone further up
shore

Lookalikes:
Laurencia obtusa
is a more bushy-
looking plant,
fronds more
cylindrical and
branching in a
spiral fashion

This species looks quite different according to its situation. In sheltered sites the fronds are long, flattened and dullish red. Further up the shore it can form a living carpet across large areas of exposed, well-lit rocks. Here the fronds are much shorter, brownish-yellow, and the branching crowded and more fleshy, with a rather crisped appearance. Plants are at their best in early spring and are said to have a peppery taste. It occurs from mid-tide level downwards around Britain and along the North Sea and Atlantic coasts of Europe.

J	F	M	A	M	J
J	A	S	O	N	D

A Red Seaweed
Nitophyllum punctatum

ID FACT FILE

TYPE:
Red

SIZE:
Frond usually
10–15 cm long,
sometimes up to
1 m or more

DESCRIPTION:
Fronds rose-pink,
very thin and
membranous,
arising singly or
in tufts from a
discoid holdfast.
Ends of fronds
split up into
blunt-ended
lobes. In water
patches of pur-
ple
iridescence are
often visible

HABITAT:
Lower shore

LOOKALIKES:
Polyneura hilliae
is thicker, of a
darker shade of
pink, and with a
broader and
more fan-shaped
frond

With its rose-pink colour this is one of the most
attractive of the red seaweeds, most of which
are very dark. The fronds are extremely thin
being only one cell thick, and rather like Purple
Laver, *Porphyra umbilicalis*, see page 40, in
texture. Flecks of a beautiful purplish-blue
iridescence are frequently visible against the
pink of the frond when in water, a characteristic
shared with Carragheen, *Chondrus crispus*, see
page 43. *N. punctatum* is an annual, and its
reproductive bodies start to appear around the
end of March. It grows on rocks and larger
seaweeds around all European coasts.

ALGAE

Red Epiphyte
Polysiphonia lanosa

ID FACT FILE

TYPE:
Red

SIZE:
Frond to 5 cm
long

DESCRIPTION:
Forming dense,
dark reddish-
brown matted
tufts consisting
of numerous
thread-like fronds
which branch at
progressively
more regular
intervals from
the base
upwards

HABITAT:
Middle shore

LOOKALIKES:
None

This small seaweed is easily recognised
because it occurs solely as an epiphyte on the
fronds of Knotted Wrack, *Ascophyllum
nodosum*, see page 19. Wherever broad
carpets of this wrack are formed it seems that
this dark brown epiphyte occurs in almost
equal quantities, so thickly does it often
encumber the fronds of the wrack, which is
sometimes almost invisible beneath. When the
tide comes in, the large bladders of the wrack
lift its living coat upwards towards the light.

ALGAE

Purple Laver
Porphyra umbilicalis

ID FACT FILE

TYPE:
Red

SIZE:
Frond to 20 cm
high and broad

DESCRIPTION:
Fronds very
broad and thin,
rosy-purple to
bright purple,
olive-green or
dirty brownish-
grey. Edge of
frond broadly
undulate, shape
variable, often
like a lettuce leaf

HABITAT:
Most levels of
the shore

LOOKALIKES:
None

Purple Laver often occurs in vast quantities on exposed rocks where its fragile appearance belies its ability to withstand the pounding of the waves. The preference for an exposed position can make it difficult to see this plant at its best when in water, as it oftens avoids the shelter of rock pools. All you normally see is great swathes of the very thin, almost transparent fronds moulding themselves against the rocks when high and dry. Purple Laver is at its best in winter, and is found throughout the coasts of northern Europe. In Wales it is made into 'Laver bread'.

ALGAE

Cactusweed

Gelidium latifolium

J	F	M	A	M	J
J	A	S	O	N	D

ID FACT FILE

TYPE:
Red

SIZE:
Frond up to
80 cm long

DESCRIPTION:
Fronds flattened,
stems ribbon-
like, branching
and with each
branch bearing
smaller
branchlets to
give a profile
similar to a large
Candelabra
cactus. Colour
red; yellow in
bright light

HABITAT:
Lower shore

LOOKALIKES:
Slender
Cactusweed,
G. sesquipedale
is similarly
branched but
has much
narrower stems

Cactusweed is most likely to be found in a turf-like fringe around the vertical edge of a rock pool on the lower shore. In such a position, where the light intensity in summertime is usually very high, the plants will be bleached, and the colour will be a pale yellowish-brown (see illustration below), rather than the rather blackish-crimson more typical in areas of lower light intensity further down the shore. Cactusweed is a common plant around all the coasts of northern Europe; in Britain it is most abundant in the south.

ALGAE

J	F	M	A	M	J
J	A	S	O	N	D

A Red Seaweed
Callophyllis laciniata

ID FACT FILE

TYPE:
Red

SIZE:
Frond up to
25 cm long,
3 cm wide

DESCRIPTION:
Frond flattened,
irregularly
branched, dull
red to light pink
(greenish where
well lit), fringed
by short
branches

HABITAT:
Lowest part of
the shore and
sublittoral zone

LOOKALIKES:
See Red Rags,
Dilsea carnosa,
page 28; and
Dulse, *Palmaria
palmata*,
page 35

This attractive and widespread seaweed is mostly found offshore in the sublittoral zone, although it is often found higher up the shore as freshly cast-up pieces which demand attention by their distinctive appearance. However, it may also form a dense carpet on the rocks on the lowest part of the shore exposed to spring tides, especially when these drop below the normal datum point into the 'minus' zone, as often happens in March and April.

ALGAE

Carragheen
Chondrus crispus

ID FACT FILE

TYPE:
Red

SIZE:
Frond to 15 cm
long

DESCRIPTION:
Fronds flattened,
dividing to form
wedge-shaped
blunt-ended
branches to give
a rather tree-like
outline. Colour
dark red to pale
yellow

HABITAT:
Lower shore, on
rocks

LOOKALIKES:
See Grapeweed,
*Mastocarpus
stellatus*, see
page 44

When seen in the clear water of a rock pool the
fronds of Carragheen exhibit an almost unique
property in that the tips of the fronds display a
striking violet iridescence. This is immediately
lost when the plant is taken out of water. On
the lower shore and in shaded situations the
fronds are purplish-red, but like many red
seaweeds, there is a very strong tendency to
turn green in strongly illuminated situations.
Carragheen, also known as 'Irish Moss' is
edible and is also used medicinally. It is found
on most northern European coasts.

ALGAE

J	F	M	A	M	J
J	A	S	O	N	D

ID FACT FILE

TYPE:
Red

SIZE:
Frond to 13 cm
long

DESCRIPTION:
Fronds blackish-
purple to bright
green, growing in
dense tufts,
stems strap-like
and with
incurved edges
forming a gutter.
Reproductive
bodies resemble
grape pips

HABITAT:
Lower shore

LOOKALIKES:
See Carragheen,
*Chondrus
crispus*, see
page 43

Grapeweed
Mastocarpus stellatus

Grapeweed often covers the rocks on the lower
shore, but is only likely to be seen on spring
tides when the water recedes far enough to
expose it. Walking down the shore, the first
plants to be encountered will be bright green
or yellowish-purple, these being exposed to
more sunlight than those lower down, which
are dark blackish-purple. The upper parts of
the fronds, on both sides, are covered with
dozens of reproductive bodies resembling
grape pips. This plant, which has been used as
a source of agar is common all around the
northern European coasts.

J	F	M	A	M	J
J	A	S	O	N	D

Sea Ivory
Ramalina siliquosa

ID FACT FILE

SIZE:
To about 10 cm
long

DESCRIPTION:
Thallus consists
of tuft of narrow,
strap-like greyish-
white ligaments,
which can be
erect or hang
downwards.
Surface often
pitted and
uneven, with
numerous small
tubercles

HABITAT:
On rock faces
and walls near
the sea

LOOKALIKES:
R. cuspidata has
more cylindrical
branches with a
smooth surface
and a blackened
base

This is one of the most abundant and
characteristic lichens of rocky sea coasts.
Thousands upon thousands of greyish-white
tufts often form a sward on rock faces and
walls near the sea. The branches are usually
only a few centimetres long, but sometimes
groups of specimens occur on vertical rock
faces in which all the plants have long, pendant
branches hanging down in curtain-like
tresses. This very common species is found on
all the coasts of northern Europe.

LICHENS

J	F	M	A	M	J
J	A	S	O	N	D

Crab's Eyes Lichen
Ochrolechia parella

ID FACT FILE

SIZE:
To 20 cm across

DESCRIPTION:
Thallus broad, flat, greyish-white, warty, usually with numerous darker greyish-black fruiting bodies (apothecia)

HABITAT:
Cliff tops

LOOKALIKES:
None

This can be a very abundant lichen on hard, acid rocks on the Atlantic coasts of western Britain and Europe, where it forms (with one or two other pale-coloured lichens) a broad so-called 'gray zone' in which the rocks appear to have been whitewashed. This 'gray zone' occurs above the so-called 'yellow zone' in which the Yellow Splash Lichen, *Xanthoria parietina*, see opposite, is dominant. The dark, pale-rimmed apothecia that are usually present in numbers on the thallus of *O. parella* resemble the eyes of crabs, hence the common name.

LICHENS

Yellow Splash Lichen
Xanthoria parietina

ID FACT FILE

SIZE:
Up to 10 cm or
more across

DESCRIPTION:
Thallus bright
golden yellow or
yellowish-orange,
composed of
numerous broad,
flattish, rather
shell-like lobes.
Darker yellow
crater-like
apothecia usually
present

HABITAT:
On rocks and
trees near the
sea; also inland

LOOKALIKES:
*Caloplaca
thallincola* is
much smaller,
paler yellow,
flatter and with
elongated
marginal lobes
divided by almost
parallel furrows

From a distance the rocks above the splash
zone on hard coastal cliffs often appear to have
been daubed with yellow paint due to the
presence of thousands of plants of this lichen
joining up to form an almost continuous
carpet. The branches and twigs of nearby trees
and bushes may also be clothed with yellow as
this very common species seems equally at
home on wood or rock. *X. parietina* is also one
of the commonest lichens inland, but it is
always far more abundant and luxuriant on
coastal rocks throughout northern Europe.

VASCULAR PLANTS

Sea Spleenwort
Asplenium marinum

J	F	M	A	M	J
J	A	S	O	N	D

ID FACT FILE

SIZE:
To 30 cm long

DESCRIPTION:
Leaves shiny
bright green,
forming small
tufts, rather
tough and
leathery, with a
brown stalk. The
spore-cases form
rows along the
side veins of the
undersides of
the leaflets

HABITAT:
Coastal cliffs

LOOKALIKES:
Black
Spleenwort, *A.
adiantum-nigrum*
has a shiny black
stem and
spore-heaps in
the centre of the
leaflets

This attractive little glossy bright-green fern
forms dense compact tufts on shady sea cliffs,
especially where there is a permanent trickle of
water seeping down across the rocks. In the
damp shady mouths of sea caves and old mine
workings it can form striking, brilliant green
carpets, but more often occurs just as one or
two plants in a favourable spot, usually in
shade. Sea Spleenwort occurs widely around
British coasts, but in England is absent from
much of the east coast and eastern Channel
coast; also found along the Atlantic coasts
of Europe.

VASCULAR PLANTS

J	F	M	A	M	J
J	A	S	O	N	D

Yellow Horned-poppy
Glaucium flavum

ID FACT FILE

HEIGHT:
To 65 cm

DESCRIPTION:
Leaves silvery grey, forming clumps, with distinctive wavy edges. Flower bright lemon yellow, 6–9 cm across. Seed pod long and horn-like

HABITAT:
Mostly on shingle; sometimes on sea walls

FLOWERING TIME:
June–September

LOOKALIKES:
None

This is one of the most attractive plants of shingle beaches and banks around our shores, sometimes occurring in thousands in favoured localities, especially on the east coast of England. The grey-green leaves with their wavy edges are very characteristic, enabling a sure identification even when no flowers are present earlier in the summer. Like all poppies, the yellow flowers are quite ephemeral and the petals soon fall. The narrow sickle-like seed pods can be as much as 30 cm long. Found on most European coasts.

VASCULAR PLANTS

English Scurvy-grass
Cochlearia anglica

J	F	M	A	M	J
J	A	S	O	N	D

ID FACT FILE

HEIGHT:
20–40 cm

DESCRIPTION:
Stems usually
sprawling on the
mud, topped by
clusters of white
flowers
10–14 mm
across. Leaves
rather long and
narrow, the
uppermost
clasping the
stem. Seed
pod ovoid

HABITAT:
Muddy shores

FLOWERING TIME:
April–May

LOOKALIKES:
See other
scurvy-grasses

This is one of three scurvy-grasses found
around our coasts and is the only one that is
restricted to muddy shores, where it is a
characteristic element of the saltmarsh flora.
It is a more sprawling plant than Common
Scurvy-grass, which is also found in
saltmarshes, although it prefers the drier parts
away from the bare mud. English Scurvy-grass
can instantly be recognised by the much longer
and narrower leaves. It is common on muddy
shores throughout northern Europe.

J	F	M	A	M	J
J	A	S	O	N	D

Common Scurvy-grass
Cochlearia officinalis

ID FACT FILE

HEIGHT:
10–25 cm

DESCRIPTION:
Plant more or less upright, hairless, with dark green, rather fleshy heart-shaped or kidney-shaped leaves on long stalks. Flowers 8–10 mm across, white (sometimes lilac) in dense clusters. Seed pod globular

HABITAT:
Mostly cliff tops, also saltmarshes

FLOWERING TIME:
April–August

LOOKALIKES:
See other scurvy-grasses

Common Scurvy-grass is much the most attractive of our three coastal species. It makes a magnificent sight when massed together in white drifts on an open cliff top, when the air for some distance around will be filled with its sweet fragrance, one of the most delightful attributes of this common plant. Although mainly found in cliff-top grassland, it also inhabits the drier parts of saltmarshes and is increasingly colonising winter-salted roadsides far inland. It also occurs on certain mountains and is found along all northern European coasts.

J	F	M	A	M	J
J	A	S	O	N	D

Early Scurvy-grass
Cochlearia danica

ID FACT FILE

HEIGHT:
5–10 cm

DESCRIPTION:
Stems prostrate, hairless, with lower leaves more or less heart-shaped, upper leaves ivy-like, all stalked. Flowers white or lilac, 4–5 mm across, in small clusters. Seed pod egg-shaped and globular

HABITAT:
Anywhere near the sea except muddy shores

FLOWERING TIME:
February–September

LOOKALIKES:
See other scurvy-grasses

Unlike the other scurvy-grasses this widespread species is prostrate and forms low, spreading mats in seaside turf, on shingle and in many other places near the sea. It is also increasing rapidly on roadsides inland, especially along motorway verges where salty water is sprayed up by passing vehicles in winter. On very exposed coasts the plants are very tiny and star the ground with their white or lilac flowers. All three of these common coastal scurvy-grasses hybridise quite freely, so some plants may be intermediate in character.

VASCULAR PLANTS

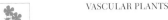

J	F	M	A	M	J
J	A	S	O	N	D

Wild Cabbage

Brassica oleracea

ID FACT FILE

HEIGHT:
30–70 cm

DESCRIPTION:
Mature stem
stout, woody.
Leaves
broadening out
towards the tips,
fleshy, greyish.
Flowers yellow,
25 mm across,
in upright spikes.
Seed pod
slender, 5–10 cm
long, with a short
beak

HABITAT:
Cliffs

FLOWERING TIME:
May–August

LOOKALIKES:
Black mustard,
B. nigra has
much smaller,
darker yellow
flowers and
smaller seed
pods (12–20
mm) that clasp
the stem. See
also Sea Radish,
*Raphanus
raphanistrum*,
page 54

A rugged cliff face decorated with numerous stout, colourful plants of Wild Cabbage in full flower is a fine sight although not a common one. In the British Isles it is almost restricted to the south and west coasts of England and Wales, although always very scattered and patchy in occurrence. In Europe it is found along the Atlantic coastline in suitable areas. Plants may also be found looking quite natural inland and on coasts outside the natural range, but these are always escapes from cultivation, Wild Cabbage being the ancestor of many 'greens'.

Sea Radish

Raphanus raphanistrum ssp *maritimus*

ID FACT FILE

HEIGHT:
20–80 cm

DESCRIPTION:
Plant bushy, rather coarse, with very rough and bristly erect stems, branching or simple. Leaves bright green, rough, not glaucous. Flowers pale yellow, petals long and narrow. Pods egg-timer-shaped

HABITAT:
On cliff tops, shingle and the tops of sandy shores

FLOWERING TIME:
June–August

LOOKALIKES:
Black mustard, *Brassica nigra* has smaller, deeper yellow flowers with short, broad petals and slimmer pods. See also Wild Cabbage, *B. oleracea*, page 53

With their long, slender, pale yellow petals arranged to form an obvious cross, the flowers of this plant are quite unlike any other yellow-flowered members of the cabbage family found either inland or near the coast. Sea Radish is also much the roughest of these and is quite unpleasant to the touch, making it unwise to push through a large stand of plants when clad only in shorts. The seed pods are highly distinctive, being rather like an hourglass, with a seed bulging in each of the two ends. Sea Radish is found widely around the coasts of northern Europe; in Britain it is commonest in the southwest.

J	F	M	A	M	J
J	A	S	O	N	D

Sea Rocket

Cakile maritima

ID FACT FILE

Height:
15–45 cm

Description:
Stems upright or
rather sprawling.
Leaves fleshy,
bright green,
smooth and
shiny, deeply
lobed. Flowers
lilac, 12–20 mm
across, in small
clusters

Habitat:
On sand and
shingle

Flowering time:
June–August

Lookalikes:
None

Sea Rocket is one of the most attractive plants
found on the tops of beaches, whether sand or
shingle. Unfortunately pressure from summer
visitors has eliminated this plant from a
number of beaches where it used to occur, and
it has decreased greatly at others, although it
sometimes reappears from dormant seed after
a lapse of several years. Large plants may be
1 m or more across, and make a splendid
sight with their masses of pale lilac flowers.
Distribution includes most European coasts.

VASCULAR PLANTS

Sea Kale
Crambe maritima

ID FACT FILE

HEIGHT:
40–60 cm

DESCRIPTION:
Stem stout and
woody at base.
Leaves thick and
fleshy, dark
bluish-green,
broad and
'cabbagy' with
wavy edges.
Flowers 10–16
mm across,
white, in large,
broad clusters.
Pods spherical

HABITAT:
On sand and
shingle,
sometimes
on cliffs

FLOWERING TIME:
May–August

LOOKALIKES:
None

Sea Kale forms massive clumps at the tops of
shingle or sandy beaches. The broad, bluish
leaves with their crinkled margins are very
attractive in their own right and enable this
handsome plant to be identified at any time.
This is even easier when the plants are
transformed by their large clusters of white,
sweetly perfumed flowers, which are very
attractive to insects. Sea Kale has often been
eaten in the past, and today is occasionally
cultivated in 'forcing' sheds. It is scattered
around most of the northern European coasts.

VASCULAR PLANTS

J	F	M	A	M	J
J	A	S	O	N	D

Sea Campion

Silene uniflora

ID FACT FILE

HEIGHT:
8–25 cm

DESCRIPTION:
Stems perennial, with a branching woody stock, forming a low cushion at flowering time. Leaves fairly narrow, greyish-green. Flowers white, 20–25 mm across

HABITAT:
On cliffs and shingle

FLOWERING TIME:
June–August

LOOKALIKES:
None on sea cliffs and shingle

Sea Campion has often been thought of as a form of Bladder Campion, *S. vulgaris*, but these days is generally regarded as a separate species restricted to coasts. The flowers are much larger and a purer white than in Bladder Campion, which also grows near the sea, but in grassland back from the cliff tops rather than in the spray zone on the cliffs themselves, where Sea Campion often forms huge swathes. Bladder Campion is much less attractive and the flowers tend to droop somewhat. Sea Campion is abundant around all the coasts of northern Europe.

VASCULAR PLANTS

J	F	M	A	M	J
J	A	S	O	N	D

Sea Sandwort
Honckenya peploides

ID FACT FILE

HEIGHT:
5–25 cm

DESCRIPTION:
Stems prostrate, hairless, with numerous very fleshy, pale yellowish-green, more or less triangular leaves up the stem. Flower whitish, 6–10 mm across. Fruits resembling small peas

HABITAT:
On sand and shingle

FLOWERING TIME:
May–July

LOOKALIKES:
None

Sea Sandwort is a very distinctive plant that can hardly be confused with anything else found at the tops of the sandy and shingly shores where it lives. It characteristically forms a low, dense, yellowish-green sward covered with small white flowers, soon succeeded by hundreds of green pea-like fruits. The small, triangular leaves are very fleshy. A mat of creeping roots anchors the plants firmly in place, enabling them to become established on the shifting fore-dunes, helping to stabilise the sand. Found on all European coasts.

J	F	M	A	M	J
J	A	S	O	N	D

Greater Sea-spurrey
Spergularia media

ID FACT FILE

HEIGHT:
Plant trailing on
ground

DESCRIPTION:
A sprawling plant
with stems up to
30 cm long
arising from a
stout, branching
rootstock.
Leaves narrow,
pointed, 1–2 cm
long. Flower
9–12 mm
across, pale
violet-pink

HABITAT:
Saltmarshes

FLOWERING TIME:
June–September

LOOKALIKES:
Sand-spurrey,
S. rubra has
shorter leaves
and smaller
(3–5mm) pinker
flowers; it may
grow in bare
ground near
the sea. See
also Rock
Sea-Spurrey,
S. rupicola,
page 60

The low, sprawling stems of Greater
Sea-spurrey usually occur on the bare mud at
the top of saltmarshes. Here they are often
mixed in among equal numbers of Lesser
Sea-spurrey, *S. marina*, which is the plant with
smaller (only 6–7 mm across), deeper pink
flowers seen on the right in the illustration
below. The larger, paler flower on the left
belongs to Greater Sea-spurrey. Both plants
are widespread around European coasts, but
S. marina pushes further up the shore into the
drier regions of the saltmarsh.

VASCULAR PLANTS

J	F	M	A	M	J
J	A	S	O	N	D

Rock Sea-spurrey
Spergularia rupicola

ID FACT FILE

HEIGHT:
Plant prostrate

DESCRIPTION:
Stems trailing,
5–20 cm long,
usually purplish,
with a woody
stock, stickily
hairy. Leaves
narrow, fleshy,
5–15 mm long,
flattened with a
horny tip. Flower
bright pink,
8–10 mm across

HABITAT:
On cliffs, rocks
and walls near
the sea

FLOWERING TIME:
June–September

LOOKALIKES:
See Greater
Sea-spurrey,
S. media,
page 59

Rock Sea-spurrey is by far the most
conspicuous and attractive of the seaside
species of *Spergularia*. It is also the only one
commonly found on dry, open cliffs and walls,
although the Lesser and Greater Sea-spurreys
may sometimes be found growing in brackish
flushes at the base of cliffs. The bright pink
flowers of Rock Sea-spurrey contrast
beautifully with the purplish flower buds. In
Britain this plant is absent from most of the
east coast, while in Europe it occurs from
northern France southwards; not in Ireland.

J	F	M	A	M	J
J	A	S	O	N	D

Tree Mallow
Lavatera arborea

ID FACT FILE

HEIGHT:
60–300 cm

DESCRIPTION:
Stem upright, forming a woody miniature trunk up to 2.5 cm in diameter. Leaves softly downy, ivy-shaped with wavy edges, to 20 cm across. Flowers bright pink, 3–4 cm across, with very dark centres

HABITAT:
Cliffs and waste places near the sea

FLOWERING TIME:
July–September

LOOKALIKES:
Common Mallow, *Malva sylvestris* is smaller, usually sprawling, leaves smaller, thinner and not softly downy; flower with petals narrow at base, leaving gaps between them and no dark centre

Often forming small thickets, Tree Mallow is one of the most statuesque of our seaside plants. Unfortunately it is rather local, being found mainly up the west coast of Britain, probably introduced on the east coast, and is absent from Ireland. In Europe it occurs from the Channel coast of France southwards. The plants are perennial, and when spikes of the bright pink flowers are present they make a striking sight. These differ from those of all other mallows by having dark centres with four green spots arranged in a square.

VASCULAR PLANTS

J	F	M	A	M	J
J	A	S	O	N	D

English Stonecrop
Sedum anglicum

ID FACT FILE

HEIGHT:
2–5 cm

DESCRIPTION:
Forming mats of
stubby little
greyish, green or
pinkish leaves on
short stems.
Star-like flowers
prolific, white,
often tinged pink,
on short stalks
in clusters

HABITAT:
Cliff tops, rocks,
walls, sand and
shingle, mainly
near the sea

FLOWERING TIME:
June–August

LOOKALIKES:
White Stonecrop,
S. album often
escapes from
gardens and is
twice as tall with
longer, cylindrical
leaves and whiter
flowers that
droop in bud

Broad mats of this pretty little plant often
carpet exposed rocky cliff tops along the
western coasts of Britain and throughout
Ireland. In the west it is also common inland
on granite tors and on walls, but this is a rare
plant inland over most of Britain and very
rare on the south and east coasts, although
widespread in mainland Europe. As summer
progresses the leaves turn to a fairly deep
shade of pink, especially in plants exposed to
intense sunlight in open, rocky places.

VASCULAR PLANTS

J	F	M	A	M	J
J	A	S	O	N	D

Sea Holly
Eryngium maritimum

ID FACT FILE

HEIGHT:
30–60 cm

DESCRIPTION:
A stiff, hairless perennial, creeping widely, with unmistakable bluish-green very spiny leaves with white veins and margins. Flower-heads globular, spiny, blue

HABITAT:
On sand and shingle

FLOWERING TIME:
July–August

LOOKALIKES:
None

Sea Holly is one of the most distinctive and attractive plants found on the coast. Although found on both sand and shingle, it is most abundant on sand dunes where extensive stands of this handsome bluish plant may occur, but only on the fore-dunes where the sand is still unstable. Sea Holly soon disappears from the stabilised dunes landward. The tiny bright blue flowers are crammed together in a more or less globular head and are most attractive to insects. Distribution includes all northern European coasts.

VASCULAR PLANTS

Wild Celery
Apium graveolens

J	F	M	A	M	J
J	A	S	O	N	D

ID FACT FILE

HEIGHT:
30–60 cm

DESCRIPTION:
Plant erect, hairless, smelling pungently of celery, yellowish-green, with a grooved stem and shiny leaves resembling those of garden celery, with large, toothed leaflets. Flowers tiny, white, in a rather open umbel. Fruits tiny, spherical

HABITAT:
Saltmarshes and brackish ditches

FLOWERING TIME:
June–August

LOOKALIKES:
Several, but never smelling pungently of celery

Most beginners to botany despair of ever mastering the identification of the so-called 'white-flowered umbellifers' in the parsley family, and simply give up. Fortunately Wild Celery has one simple characteristic that enables a quick and easy identification – a strong smell of celery. This is so pungent, permeating the area for some distance around when the plants occur in quantity, that you know that you have found Wild Celery without even needing to take a closer look. It is found on most coasts in northern Europe.

VASCULAR PLANTS

J	F	M	A	M	J
J	A	S	O	N	D

Alexanders
Smyrnium olusatrum

ID FACT FILE

HEIGHT:
50–150 cm

DESCRIPTION:
Plant hairless.
Stem stout,
solid, furrowed,
upright, rather
bushy. Leaves
shiny, dark
glossy green,
divided into three
stalked lobes.
Flower yellow, in
crowded umbels.
Fruits black,
conspicuous

HABITAT:
Lanesides,
hedgebanks and
waste places
near the sea

FLOWERING TIME:
April–June

LOOKALIKES:
None flowering
so early

Alexanders is not native to the coasts of
northern Europe but has long been thoroughly
naturalised in many areas after escaping from
cultivation, having formerly been cultivated as
a pot-herb. This distinctive member of the
parsley family has now made itself so much a
part of the coastal landscape that the presence
of large stands of this tall, glossy green plant
along the roadsides announce that the sea must
be close by, although isolated plants also occur
quite far inland.

Rock Samphire

Crithmum maritimum

J	F	M	A	M	J
J	A	S	O	N	D

ID FACT FILE

HEIGHT:
15–30 cm

DESCRIPTION:
Plant hairless.
Stems narrow,
branching, bushy
and rather squat.
Leaves fleshy,
narrowly cut into
numerous
untoothed
leaflets. Flowers
tiny, yellowish, in
crowded umbels.
Fruit egg-shaped,
ridged

HABITAT:
Cliffs, rocks and
seawalls;
sometimes on
sand and shingle

FLOWERING TIME:
July–September

LOOKALIKES:
None

Cliff faces, sea walls and rocky outcrops all along the coasts of northern Europe are decorated with the rather low, bushy plants of Rock Samphire, which in late summer will be covered with umbels of tiny yellowish flowers. Despite their lack of gaudiness, these flowers nevertheless manage to attract plenty of hoverflies and other insects. The narrow fleshy leaves make this plant instantly recognisable, and can be pickled and eaten, although this trade is not as common as it used to be.

VASCULAR PLANTS

Wild Carrot
Daucus carota

J	F	M	A	M	J
J	A	S	O	N	D

ID FACT FILE

HEIGHT:
15–100 cm

DESCRIPTION:
Stem erect, solid, ridged. Leaves feathery, shortly hairy. Flowers dirty white, tiny, massed together in broad, flat-topped umbels; flower in centre of umbel deep red. Fruits spiny, fruiting-head crowding inward to form a hollow

HABITAT:
In cliff-top grassland; also inland

FLOWERING TIME:
June–August

LOOKALIKES:
Many other white-flowered umbellifers but none with feathery leaves and red flower in centre

Grassy cliff slopes are often covered with thousands of plants of Wild Carrot, showing up as a white patch from a distance when the flowers are present. Wild Carrot, from which the cultivated carrot has been derived, is also found in dry, grassy places far inland, but on the coast the plants are lower, stouter and fleshier. The presence of a single deep red flower in the centre of the umbel is usually a sure guide to identity, but can be absent, when the feathery leaves are a giveaway. Wild Carrot is common throughout most of northern Europe.

VASCULAR PLANTS

J	F	M	A	M	J
J	A	S	O	N	D

Common Sea-lavender
Limonium vulgare

The bare, flat expanses of our coastal saltmarshes can be bleak and uninviting places at most times of the year. Yet from July onwards many of them are transformed into brilliant carpets of purple as thousands of plants of Common Sea-lavender come into flower. The best displays are found on the east coast of England, although this attractive plant is scattered in suitable habitats around the coasts of Britain and Europe (although absent from Ireland, where *L. humile* is common). It is not related to the lavender grown in gardens.

ID FACT FILE

HEIGHT:
10–40 cm

DESCRIPTION:
Plant perennial, stem erect, rounded, branching, bushy. Leaves green on top, paler beneath. Flowers small, purple, crowded together in many-branched heads on long stems

HABITAT:
Saltmarshes on muddy shores

FLOWERING TIME:
July–October

LOOKALIKES:
Lax-flowered Sea-lavender, *L. humile,* also from saltmarshes, has smaller flowers, all up the stem and not crowded together in heads. See also Rock Sea-lavender, *L. binervosum,* opposite

Rock Sea-lavender
Limonium binervosum

J	F	M	A	M	J
J	A	S	O	N	D

ID FACT FILE

HEIGHT:
5–50 cm

DESCRIPTION:
Plant perennial, with branched woody stock and erect, hairless flowering stems. Leaves numerous, variable in shape, from broadly to narrowly tongue-like. Flowering stems wavy, flowers purple, in crowded heads

HABITAT:
Rocky cliffs

FLOWERING TIME:
July–September

LOOKALIKES:
See Common Sea-lavender, *L. vulgare*, opposite

This is a much smaller, daintier plant than Common Sea-lavender. *L. vulgare*, see opposite, and on very exposed clifftops the plants are only a few centimetres high. In some places the open, stony cliff slopes are covered with a haze of purple when the plant is in flower. Rock Sea-lavender likes to feel the salty spray on its leaves, and only thrives on the open rocks of the wave-splashed cliffs. The wavy nature of the flowering stem is very distinctive. This plant is found widely around British coasts, but is very rare in Scotland and Ireland. In Europe it occurs from France southwards.

VASCULAR PLANTS

J	F	M	A	M	J
J	A	S	O	N	D

ID FACT FILE

HEIGHT:
5–25 cm

DESCRIPTION:
Forming dense
tufts, with
cushions of
rather fleshy
leaves which are
long and slender.
Flowers small,
pink, crowded
together to form
conspicuous
pompom heads

HABITAT:
Rocks, cliffs,
walls, pastures
and saltmarshes
near the sea

FLOWERING TIME:
May–September

LOOKALIKES:
None

Thrift
Armeria maritima

When present in its normal dense stands
Thrift, which is in the same family as the
Sea-lavenders, is one of the most spectacular
sights on the coast when the plants are in full
flower. This mainly takes place in May and
June, although a few flowers can be seen right
through until autumn. The shade of pink varies
greatly, from a beautiful deep shade of
rose-pink to rather wishy-washy shades of
pinkish-white. Plants growing side by side can
vary greatly in this respect. Thrift occurs on all
the coasts of northern Europe and is one of the
commonest seaside plants.

J	F	M	A	M	J
J	A	S	O	N	D

Sea-milkwort
Glaux maritima

ID FACT FILE

HEIGHT:
Plant sprawls

DESCRIPTION:
Plant hairless, shiny. Stems trailing, 10–30 cm long. Leaves opposite along the stem, 4–12 mm long, narrowly oval, fleshy. Flowers pink, 5 mm across

HABITAT:
Saltmarshes, on rocks and in damp gulleys near the sea

FLOWERING TIME:
June–July

LOOKALIKES:
None

This charming little plant is a member of the primrose family. Despite its common name, Sea-milkwort is not related to the true milkworts (various species of *Polygala*), which may grow quite close by in short cliff-top grassland. With its abundance of tiny pink flowers and trailing stems, Sea-milkwort cannot really be mistaken for any other plant. It is most common on saltmarshes, particularly on bare mud around the edges, but also occurs on the tops of rocks at cliff bases and in damp flushes. It is common on all the coasts of northern Europe.

J	F	M	A	M	J
J	A	S	O	N	D

ID FACT FILE

HEIGHT:
Plant prostrate

DESCRIPTION:
Plant hairless.
Stems long,
slender, creeping
across the sand.
Leaves rather
fleshy, kidney-
shaped, on long
slender stalks.
Flowers solitary,
funnel-shaped,
55 mm across,
pink, with white
stripes

HABITAT:
On sandy shores,
occasionally on
shingle

FLOWERING TIME:
June–August

LOOKALIKES:
Field Bindweed,
*Convolvulus
arvensis* has
much smaller
pink or white
flowers only
2 cm across
and arrow- or
halberd-shaped
leaves

Sea Bindweed
Calystegia soldanella

Coming across the large pink funnel-shaped
flowers of Sea Bindweed scattered across a
dune slope or at the top of a sandy beach is
always a pleasure. These striking flowers are
very popular with bumble bees. Even without
flowers, this species is easy to recognise on
account of the fleshy, kidney-shaped leaves,
quite unlike those of Field Bindweed, a
troublesome garden weed that may also be
found on the coast. Sea Bindweed is scattered
around the coasts of northern Europe.

J	F	M	A	M	J
J	A	S	O	N	D

Sea Plantain
Plantago maritima

ID FACT FILE

HEIGHT:
2–20 cm

DESCRIPTION:
Plant perennial,
normally hair-
less. Leaves
5–30 cm long,
in a basal tuft,
bright green
flesh, long and
narrow, strap-
like, tapering at
the tip. Flowers
minute, crammed
together in a
greenish spike
3–8 cm long

HABITAT:
On cliffs and salt-
marshes near
the sea

FLOWERING TIME:
June–August

LOOKALIKES:
See Buck's-horn
Plantain,
P. coronopus,
page 74

Tall plants of Sea Plantain are often common
in saltmarshes on muddy shores. Much smaller
plants occcur on cliff faces, in cliff-top grassland
and on adjacent drystone walls. In really
exposed positions on north-facing cliffs the
entire flowering plant may crouch low down
against the wind and be only around 2 cm tall.
When in full flower Sea Plantain is quite
attractive as the flowers, although individually
very tiny, have conspicuous yellow anthers
which brighten up the clusters of narrow
flower spikes. Like in all plantains, the flowers
are pollinated by the wind. Sea Plantain is
found on most coasts around northern Europe.

VASCULAR PLANTS

Buck's-horn Plantain
Plantago coronopus

ID FACT FILE

HEIGHT:
5–40 mm

DESCRIPTION:
Plant downy.
Leaves 2–6 cm
long, usually
toothed along
the margins, with
just a single
vein, forming a
broad, flat
rosette. Flowers
minute,
clustered on a
spike only 5–40
mm long

HABITAT:
On bare ground
near the sea

FLOWERING TIME:
May–July

LOOKALIKES:
Ribwort Plantain,
P. lanceolata has
broader,
untoothed leaves
with 3–5
prominent ribs
below; see also
Sea Plantain,
P. maritima, see
page 73

Flattish areas of bare ground near the sea are
often covered in a dense turf-like carpet of this
small plantain, to the exclusion of most other
plants, including grasses. The softly downy
surface of the leaves gives these carpets a
characteristic shimmer in bright sunshine that
enables the species to be recognised on sight.
The flower spikes are so short and dumpy that
they scarcely add much to the plant when
present as the anthers are very pale coloured
and not conspicuous. Buck's-horn Plantain is
found around all the coasts of Europe and also,
but more rarely, inland.

Sea Beet

Beta vulgaris ssp *maritima*

J	F	M	A	M	J
J	A	S	O	N	D

ID FACT FILE

HEIGHT:
30–120 cm

DESCRIPTION:
Plant hairless, usually sprawling. Leaves very varied in shape, always shiny, dark green to reddish, rather tough and leathery. Flowers green, minute, in long narrow spikes

HABITAT:
On bare ground near the sea

FLOWERING TIME:
June–September

LOOKALIKES:
None

The sprawling, dark green untidy looking clumps of Sea Beet are a common sight around all the coasts of Europe, it being equally at home on an exposed cliff top, muddy creek-side, shingle bank or town sea wall. Wherever it grows it is always instantly recognisable, although its size and height vary enormously according to the degree of exposure to high winds and the amount of drought to be endured. In autumn it turns yellowish-orange. Both Beetroot and Sugar Beet are cultivated forms of the wild Sea Beet.

VASCULAR PLANTS

Sea-purslane
Atriplex portulacoides

J	F	M	A	M	J
J	A	S	O	N	D

ID FACT FILE

Height:
20–100 cm

Description:
A small mealy shrub, rather straggly and copiously branching, with brown stems and untoothed elliptical leaves. Flowers tiny, on small side-branches along the central spike

Habitat:
Saltmarshes

Flowering time:
July–September

Lookalikes:
None

Sea-purslane is a highly gregarious plant and is normally seen forming dense, silver-leaved stands in muddy saltmarshes, becoming very densely crowded along the margins of the many creeks that often wend their way through the broad, flat expanse of the saltmarsh. As in most members of the goosefoot family (Chenopodiaceae), the flowers individually are not up to much, but when densely crowded on the branching stems they lend an overall golden appearance to the plants. Sea-purslane is widely distributed but scattered around the coasts of Europe.

VASCULAR PLANTS

Annual Sea-blite
Suaeda maritima

ID FACT FILE

HEIGHT:
Usually prostrate

DESCRIPTION:
Plants annual,
hairless. Stems
trailing on the
mud, 7–30 cm
long. Leaves
short and fleshy,
cylindrical, bright
green, bluish-
green or reddish.
Flowers tiny

HABITAT:
On mud of
saltmarshes

FLOWERING TIME:
July–September

LOOKALIKES:
See Common
Glasswort,
*Salicornia
europaea*,
page 79

Annual Sea-blite is one of a number of not
particularly attractive members of the
goosefoot family that live in the mud of coastal
saltmarshes that are flooded twice a day by the
incoming tides. This is one of the more easily
recognised species on account of its sprawling
habit, with stems trailing across the mud,
and distinctively shaped leaves. The flowers
need searching for, being tucked away
inconspicuously near the leaf-bases. Annual
Sea-blite is found along most of the coasts of
northern Europe.

VASCULAR PLANTS

J	F	M	A	M	J
J	A	S	O	N	D

Prickly Saltwort
Salsola kali

ID FACT FILE

HEIGHT:
To 60 cm

DESCRIPTION:
A very stiff and prickly, greyish-green and densely leafy annual. Stem usually with reddish-pink stripes. Leaves 1–4 cm long, fleshy, narrowing to a short spine at the tip. Flowers tiny, greenish

HABITAT:
Sandy coasts

FLOWERING TIME:
July–September

LOOKALIKES:
None

Prickly Saltwort is a very distinctive-looking plant that is usually prostrate but can be upright and quite tall. The rather short, fat and very fleshy leaves with their glistening spiny tips are very characteristic. The tiny flowers are tucked away inconspicuously in a tuft of leaf-like bracts at the base of the leaves, and as in all members of the goosefoot family (Chenopodiaceae) are wind-pollinated. The typical habitat is along the drift-line at the top of sandy shores, almost throughout Europe.

VASCULAR PLANTS

Common Glasswort
Salicornia europaea

J	F	M	A	M	J
J	A	S	O	N	D

ID FACT FILE

HEIGHT:
5–30 cm

DESCRIPTION:
Plant erect or sprawling, prolifically branching. Stems smooth, glossy, hairless, yellowish-green, turning reddish in autumn. Leaves reduced to fleshy sheaths on stem. Flowers tiny

HABITAT:
Saltmarshes on muddy shores

FLOWERING TIME:
August–September

LOOKALIKES:
There are several similar-looking species all very difficult to tell apart. See also Annual Sea-blite, *Suaeda maritima*, page 77

Glassworts are some of the most characteristic plants of muddy shores, where they often form dense carpets which turn an attractive blushing red in autumn. The individual plants are strange and rather twig-like, with no obvious sign of leaves, these being closely moulded to the stems, making the whole thing resemble a green many-branched twig. The flowers are so minute that they are visible only as one or two stamens almost buried in the succulent stems. Common Glasswort is edible and is harvested for pickling. It is common on suitable shores throughout Europe.

VASCULAR PLANTS

J	F	M	A	M	J
J	A	S	O	N	D

Sea-buckthorn
Hippophae rhamnoides

ID FACT FILE

HEIGHT:
1–3 m

DESCRIPTION:
A small, many-branched thorny shrub with pale brown stems. Leaves rather narrow, covered with silvery scales. Flowers minute, green. Berries bright orange, ovoid

HABITAT:
Mostly on sand dunes, sometimes on cliffs or shingle

FLOWERING TIME:
April–May, before the leaves

LOOKALIKES:
None

In the British Isles Sea-buckthorn is only native around the east coast from Yorkshire to Sussex, but it has been widely planted elsewhere in an effort to stabilise shifting sand dunes. On the coasts of mainland Europe it is very widespread. It often forms dense thickets, and in areas where it has been planted it has a habit of taking over and smothering everything else – it may need to be controlled or even eliminated. Male and female flowers occur on separate plants and, in late summer, female plants are covered in masses of bright orange berries.

VASCULAR PLANTS

J	F	M	A	M	J
J	A	S	O	N	D

Portland Spurge
Euphorbia portlandica

ID FACT FILE

HEIGHT:
5–40 cm

DESCRIPTION:
A hairless, greenish-grey biennial, branching solely from the base and usually with distinctive red stems. Leaves 5–20 mm long, rather leathery, elongate-oval, tipped with a minute point. Flowers tiny

HABITAT:
Cliffs and sandy shores

FLOWERING TIME:
April–September

LOOKALIKES:
See Sea Spurge, *E. paralias*, page 82

In the British Isles Portland Spurge is classified as a Nationally Scarce Plant, being absent from the east coast and very scattered elsewhere. In mainland Europe it is spread along the Atlantic coast from France to Portugal. It is the only one out of two seaside spurges to be found on sea cliffs. Where it grows on sand, it could be confused with Sea Spurge, *E. paralias*, see page 82, with which it often grows, but is usually smaller, with many distinctive red stems and green (not grey) flat-topped (not concave) pointed (not blunt) leaves.

VASCULAR PLANTS

Sea Spurge
Euphorbia paralias

J	F	M	A	M	J
J	A	S	O	N	D

ID FACT FILE

HEIGHT:
20–40 cm

DESCRIPTION:
Plant perennial, stems greyish-green. Leaves numerous, densely arranged and overlapping up the stem, greyish-green, with a concave upper surface and tapering but blunt tip. Flowers in open umbels

HABITAT:
On sandy shores, mostly on dunes

FLOWERING TIME:
June–September

LOOKALIKES:
See Portland Spurge, *E. portlandica*, page 81

Sea Spurge is a much larger, bushier, greyer plant than Portland Spurge, E. *portlandica*, see page 81, with which it often grows. Sea Spurge is not normally found on cliffs and often comes into flower when Portland Spurge is already well past its prime. The leaves of Sea Spurge are very different, being much fleshier, grey rather than green and without the tiny point present in Portland Spurge. The way the leaves of Sea Spurge are angled only slightly away from the stem so that they almost clasp it is also very typical. Distribution includes most of the British coast, and in Europe from Belgium southwards.

J	F	M	A	M	J
J	A	S	O	N	D

Slender Thistle

Carduus tenuiflorus

ID FACT FILE

HEIGHT:
15–120 cm

DESCRIPTION:
Stems erect, covered with cottony hairs and with conspicuous spine-laden wings running up their length, branching higher up. Leaves cottony beneath. Flower-heads rather small and narrow, very spiny, pale pink

HABITAT:
Grassy places near the sea

FLOWERING TIME:
June–August

LOOKALIKES:
In Welted Thistle, *C. crispus* the stems are naked just beneath the flower-heads which are broader and more reddish-purple. Marsh Thistle, *Cirsium palustre* has dark purple, non-spiny flower-heads

The Slender Thistle, formerly often called the Seaside Thistle, is usually easy to recognise on the strength of its flower-heads, which are much narrower and of a far paler shade of pink than any other thistles. The only other spiny-stemmed, upright thistle common near the sea is the Marsh Thistle, *Cirsium palustre*, but this has non-spiny flower-heads. Creeping Thistle, *Cirsium arvense*, is widespread but its stems are not spiny. Slender Thistle is found on cliff tops, at the top of beaches and in waste places near the sea (and as a casual inland) in most of Britain and from Holland southwards.

VASCULAR PLANTS

Golden-samphire
Inula crithmoides

J	F	M	A	M	J
J	A	S	O	N	D

ID FACT FILE

HEIGHT:
15–90 cm

DESCRIPTION:
Forming stout, hairless, bright green tufts. Stems very fleshy, branching above. Leaves also fleshy, 2.4–6 cm long, up the stem, like long narrow straps, often 3-toothed at the tips. Flower-heads yellow, 2.5 cm across

HABITAT:
Cliffs, rocks, shingle banks and saltmarshes

FLOWERING TIME:
July–August

LOOKALIKES:
Common Fleabane, *Pulicaria dysenterica*, often common in damp areas near the sea, is downy all over with much broader leaves

Like many true coastal plants, Golden Samphire is both fleshy and hairless. It is our only coastal plant that has both fleshy leaves and yellow daisy-like flower-heads. These occur at the tops of the stems, which are thickly clothed all the way up with the long and narrow, bright green leaves. Golden-samphire is a far more attractive plant than Samphire, *Crithmum maritimum*, which despite the similar name is in a different family. In Britain Golden-samphire is classified as a Nationally Scarce Plant, being scattered around the south and west coasts. It is widespread on European shores.

VASCULAR PLANTS

Sea Mayweed

Tripleurospermum maritimum

J	F	M	A	M	J
J	A	S	O	N	D

ID FACT FILE

HEIGHT:
10–60 cm

DESCRIPTION:
Plant erect or
sprawling, bright
green, smooth
and shining, not
hairy. Leaves
oblong in outline,
divided 2–3
times into
segments.
Flower-heads
1.5–5 cm
across, white
with yellow
centres

HABITAT:
Anywhere near
the coast

FLOWERING TIME:
July–September

LOOKALIKES:
Scentless
Mayweed,
T. inodorum;
Oxeye Daisy,
*Leucanthemum
vulgare* is sparse-
ly hairy and has
flower-heads
3–6 cm across

Sea Mayweed, found around all European
coasts, is very similar to Scentless Mayweed,
T. inodorum, a common weed of cornfields,
farm gateways and waste places. It is doubtful
if the two are really separate species, and Sea
Mayweed has often been classed as a
subspecies of the commoner plant, and they
freely cross when occurring together. The main
difference is the rather fleshy, succulent nature
of the leaf segments in Sea Mayweed, and
there are small differences in the seeds. Oxeye
Daisy, *Leucanthemum vulgare*, which can be
common on the coast, is easily distinguished by
its far larger flowers.

VASCULAR PLANTS

Sea Aster
Aster tripolium

J	F	M	A	M	J
J	A	S	O	N	D

ID FACT FILE

HEIGHT:
15–100 cm

DESCRIPTION:
Stems stout, erect, much branched above. Leaves fleshy, 7–12 cm long, quite narrow, hairless, shiny, dark green, with a prominent midrib. Flower-heads to 20 mm across, bluish-purple

HABITAT:
Mainly salt-marshes, also cliffs

FLOWERING TIME:
July–October

LOOKALIKES:
None

When seen at its best, with the golden disc-shaped centre of its flower-heads surrounded by a frill of colourful, bluish-purple or whitish-pink rays, the Sea Aster closely resembles a garden Michaelmas Daisy. Unfortunately, in many plants of Sea Aster the colourful ray-florets are either reduced to a handful of rather ragged-looking individuals, or are absent altogether, leaving just the yellow centres. Such plants are then not particularly attractive compared with the fully flowered varieties. Sea Aster is mainly found in muddy saltmarshes, but also occurs sporadically on rocky cliffs, around the coasts of Europe.

VASCULAR PLANTS

J	F	M	A	M	J
J	A	S	O	N	D

Sea Arrowgrass
Triglochin maritima

ID FACT FILE

HEIGHT:
15–50 cm

DESCRIPTION:
A dark green, tufted, hairless perennial with long, narrow, fleshy, grass-like leaves. Flowers tiny, greenish, on very short stalks, arranged up a long, narrow spike

HABITAT:
In saltmarshes

FLOWERING TIME:
May–August

LOOKALIKES:
Marsh Arrowgrass, *T. palustris* is smaller and has narrower leaves and longer-stalked flowers on a much thinner spike

Despite its common name, Sea Arrowgrass does not belong to the family of true grasses (Poaceae), but to the much smaller arrowgrass family, Juncaginaceae. Sea Arrowgrass forms broad, dark green tufts in saltmarshes and in damp brackish spots on dunes around all the coasts of Europe. Its tiny inconspicuous flowers are arranged in a long, narrow spike which becomes more conspicuous when the flowers have been replaced by the fat, egg-shaped fruits. As in so many seaside plants, the long grass-like leaves are very fleshy.

VASCULAR PLANTS

J	F	M	A	M	J
J	A	S	O	N	D

Eelgrass
Zostera marina

As it waves gently in the shallow water just below the lower tidemark Eelgrass could easily be mistaken for a large green seaweed. However, unlike seaweeds, Eelgrass has roots, which anchor the plant in gravel, sand or mud just offshore. During very low spring tides the plants are left stranded on the shore when they can easily be inspected and you may be able to locate the minute flowers tucked away near the leaf-bases. Eelgrass is distributed around the coasts of Europe, but in many areas has declined greatly due to a recurring disease.

ID FACT FILE

HEIGHT:
Plant sprawling

DESCRIPTION:
Plant perennial. Stems branched, leaves ribbon-like, dark green, 20–100 cm long, 5–10 mm broad, pointed at the tip and with three parallel veins. Flowers minute, male and female on separate plants

HABITAT:
In the sea at and just below low-water mark

FLOWERING TIME:
June–August

LOOKALIKES:
Narrow-leaved Eelgrass, *Z. angustifolia* has narrower leaves, only 2–3 mm across

VASCULAR PLANTS

J	F	M	A	M	J
J	A	S	O	N	D

Sea Club-rush
Bolboschoenus maritimus

ID FACT FILE

HEIGHT:
30–100 cm

DESCRIPTION:
A stout, hairless perennial with sharp 3-angled stems which are quite rough towards the tip. Leaves keeled, rough on the edges. Flower-spikelets egg-shaped, dark brown

HABITAT:
In ditches and brackish grassland near the sea

FLOWERING TIME:
July–August

LOOKALIKES:
Common Club-rush, *Schoenoplectus lacustris* and Grey Club-rush, *S. tabernaemontani* are much taller and have smooth, rounded stems

A dark green very rough-textured rush-like plant forming dense stands along the edges of tidal rivers, in ditches or in long, brackish grassland near the sea, will certainly be Sea Club-rush. The coarse, grass-like leaves are flat on top, with a distinct keel beneath, and very rough margins. The tiny wind-pollinated flowers occur in dark reddish-brown egg-shaped spikelets gathered in an open group near the top of the plant and overtopped by long, narrow leaf-like bracts. Distribution includes almost all European coasts.

VASCULAR PLANTS

J	F	M	A	M	J
J	A	S	O	N	D

Common Cord-grass
Spartina anglica

ID FACT FILE

HEIGHT:
20–50 cm

DESCRIPTION:
A coarse, stout, erect and almost hairless perennial with long, smooth leaves some 4 mm wide tapering to a rather stout point. Flower-spikes 2–3 together with numerous yellowish spikelets

HABITAT:
On coastal mud flats

FLOWERING TIME:
July–September

LOOKALIKES:
Townsend's Cord-grass, *S. x townsendi*, a hybrid, can be difficult to distinguish, but is larger in all its parts

In many areas Common Cord-grass has been replaced by dense, pure stands of *S. x townsendi*, which arose as an accidental hybrid between *S. anglica* and the introduced American *S. alterniflora*. The hybrid proved to be exceptionally vigorous and has been widely planted to stabilise the mud. The native *S. anglica*, a much smaller plant with less conspicuous flowers, still holds unopposed sway in some areas, such as beside the Tamar River in Cornwall where the interloper is yet to appear.

VASCULAR PLANTS

Marram Grass
Ammophila arenaria

J	F	M	A	M	J
J	A	S	O	N	D

ID FACT FILE

HEIGHT:
60–120 cm

DESCRIPTION:
A stout, erect
perennial with
long, creeping
stems repeatedly
rooting. Leaves
broad, stout and
rigid, with
inrolled margins
and sharply
pointed tips.
Flower-heads
long and thick

HABITAT:
Sand dunes

FLOWERING TIME:
July–August

LOOKALIKES:
None

With its large tuft of broad, flat, polished
sharply pointed leaves Marram can scarcely be
confused with any other grass, especially when
the very large, plump attractive flower-heads
appear, shaped like a fox's brush and
ornamented by numerous conspicuous
whitish-yellow spikelets. Marram's habit of
sending out hordes of runners that root into
the sand at their joints enables it to quickly
colonise bare areas of shifting sand. Its role as
a pioneeer on the fore-dunes has meant it is
often planted as a binding agent. It is common
around western European coasts.

VASCULAR PLANTS

Sand Cat's Tail

Phleum arenarium

J	F	M	A	M	J
J	A	S	O	N	D

ID FACT FILE

HEIGHT:
3–15 cm

DESCRIPTION:
A tufted annual with short, smooth pale green leaves. Flower-heads rather short and dumpy, unbranched, elongated egg-shaped, tapering below, up to 5 cm long but often shorter

HABITAT:
Sand dunes and occasionally on sandy fields inland

FLOWERING TIME:
May–July

LOOKALIKES:
Timothy, *P. pratense* is common in damper, grassy places and is much larger, usually 20–120 cm high

This charming little plant often forms dense carpets on coastal dunes, although it is rather more conspicuous later in the year when the flower-heads have set seed, rather than earlier in the year when the very inconspicuous, tiny pale yellow flowers are present. It grows on the dry, well-drained parts of the dunes, among mosses and lichens, where the vegetation quickly becomes shrivelled and dry with the onset of the long, hot summer days. It is widespread on almost all European coasts.

VASCULAR PLANTS

J	F	M	A	M	J
J	A	S	O	N	D

ID FACT FILE

HEIGHT:
30–80 cm

DESCRIPTION:
A tufted, dark green evergreen with long, narrow, smooth leaves and purplish flowers with darker veins. Fruits split to reveal bright orange seeds

HABITAT:
Dunes, banks, cliffsides and roadsides, mainly on the coast

FLOWERING TIME:
June

LOOKALIKES:
None

Stinking Iris
Iris foetidissima

The tufts of smooth, shiny leaves of Stinking Iris are often conspicuous on sand dunes, alongside cliff-top paths and on roadside banks in many places near the sea in southern England and Wales, and from France eastwards to Italy and Greece. It is also found at scattered localities inland, and has been naturalised in Scotland. The flowers are relatively inconspicuous, often being almost hidden among the leaves, but are very attractive. When the oblong fruits split open in autumn they expose rows of globular, brilliant orange seeds.

VASCULAR PLANTS

J	F	M	A	M	J
J	A	S	O	N	D

Spring Squill
Scilla verna

ID FACT FILE

HEIGHT:
5–20 cm

DESCRIPTION:
A hairless
perennial bulb
with long, bright
green, narrow
grass-like leaves.
Flowers on short
stalks, pale blue,
clustered

HABITAT:
Grassy places
near the sea

FLOWERING TIME:
April–June

LOOKALIKES:
Autumn Squill,
S. autumnalis
has taller spikes
of purple flowers
which are
produced from
July to
September

It is worth making a pilgrimage to somewhere such as the coast of north Cornwall in springtime just to see the cliff-top grasslands studded with millions of blue star-like flowers of Spring Squill, one of our most charming wildflowers. Similar sights can be enjoyed in many places up the western coast of mainland Britain, and in a few places on the east coast, southward to Lincolnshire, but not along the south coast east of Devon, and only on the east coast in Ireland. In mainland Europe Spring Squill occurs from Norway southwards.

J	F	M	A	M	J
J	A	S	O	N	D

Dune Early Marsh Orchid

Dactylorhiza incarnata ssp *coccinea*

ID FACT FILE

HEIGHT:
10–20 cm

DESCRIPTION:
Leaves and
stem smooth,
pale green,
unspotted. Stem
with a large
central hollow.
Flowers intense
brick-red, looking
narrow from the
front as the
sides are folded
back, in a dense
oblong spike

HABITAT:
Sand dunes;
also inland on
lake shores in
Ireland

FLOWERING TIME:
May–July

LOOKALIKES:
None with true
brick-red flowers
as illustrated

Thousands of spikes of this very showy orchid often occur in the damp hollows or slacks of coastal sand dunes, mainly up the West coast of mainland Britain and in Ireland, being absent from the rest of Europe. The typical, inland form has pale flesh-pink flowers. Another common sand dune orchid, the Southern Marsh Orchid, *D. praetermissa* is taller and has purple flowers that look much broader as the sides are not folded back. In the Common Spotted Orchid, *D. fuchsii* the flowers are whitish with deeper pink markings. The Pyramidal Orchid, *Anacamptis pyramidalis* has shorter, dumpy pyramid-shaped spikes and pink flowers.

| J | F | M | A | M | J |
| J | A | S | O | N | D |

Breadcrumb Sponge
Halichondria panicea

ID FACT FILE

Size:
Usually about
10 cm across

Description:
Forming broad
flattish sheets or
dome-like
mounds, covered
in crater-like
structures called
oscula. Colour
variable, usually
green or orange.
Has a strong
smell

Habitat:
On rocks, shells
and seaweed
holdfasts on
lower shore

Lookalikes:
Several other
species similar
and difficult to
tell apart

Sponges are very simple animals that filter
their food from the surrounding water. The
Breadcrumb Sponge is by far the commonest
of several species of encrusting sponges found
on the lower shore. In some areas it forms
substantial structures resembling reefs, but
more often it encrusts rocks, shells and other
hard substrates on all the coasts of Europe.
Several colour forms may occur together,
especially where large mats of this sponge
cover the flattish, sheltered overhanging faces
of large rocks. *Hemimycale columella* is
another orange species and is covered in a
honeycomb-like arrangement of ridges.

SPONGES

Orangepeel Sponge
Hymeniacidon perleve

ID FACT FILE

SIZE:
5–15 cm across

DESCRIPTION:
Forming flattened orange or reddish mats that follow the contours of the substrate. Surface rough, with scattered pointed, projecting lobes and very occasional oscula

HABITAT:
On lower shore, on rocks

LOOKALIKES:
Several other species of orange encrusting sponges, which are difficult to distinguish from each other

The broad mats of this brightly coloured orange or reddish-orange sponge are a prominent sight on rock faces on the lower shore. The surface has a much smoother appearance than in the Breadcrumb Sponge, *Halichondria panicea*, see opposite, due to the presence of only a few scattered oscula across the surface, which is actually quite rough to the touch. This sponge is more resistant to prolonged drying out than most, so can be found quite a long way up the shore, especially on rock faces sheltered from direct sunlight. It is common along all the European coasts.

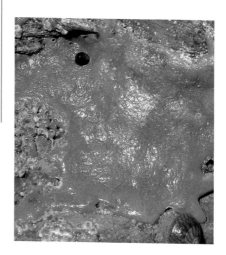

SPONGES

A Sponge
Suberites domuncula

J	F	M	A	M	J
J	A	S	O	N	D

ID FACT FILE

SIZE:
To 20 cm or
more across

DESCRIPTION:
Forming rather
broad and low,
more or less
spherical
mounds with a
wrinkled surface
like a shrivelled
apple. Colour a
dingy brownish-
yellow. Each
mound bears a
conspicuous
round opening
(osculum)

HABITAT:
Lower shore

LOOKALIKES:
S. carnosus is
more spherical

This is a large sponge that is difficult to miss,
but you will only find it on the very lowest part
of the shore, exposed solely during very low
spring tides. Then it can be quite abundant,
encrusting rocks, often with several individual
specimens occurring closely side by side to
cover quite a large area. It may also encrust the
shells adopted as homes by hermit crabs. This
sponge is said to have a rather strong smell of
sulphur. It occurs widely around the coasts
of Europe.

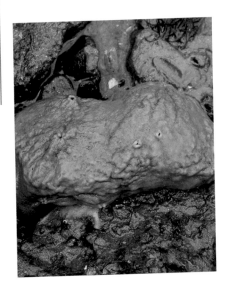

| J | F | M | A | M | J |
| J | A | S | O | N | D |

Purse Sponge
Scypha compressa

ID FACT FILE

SIZE:
Up to 2 cm high, 1 cm broad

DESCRIPTION:
Resembling a dingy greyish sac, with a large opening (osculum) at the apex. Usually forming small clumps

HABITAT:
Lower shore, on rocks, shells and large seaweeds

LOOKALIKES:
In *Sycon ciliatum* (see next page) the surface appears furry and there is a stiff collar with a fringe of spines around the terminal opening

This sponge, widespread on the coasts of northern Europe, is an annual which is present throughout the winter before releasing larvae into the water in early spring, after which the adults die off. The specimens in the illustration were photographed on 18 March, and would probably have disappeared within a month. The larvae are initially free-swimming, but soon settle on rocks, shells and large seaweeds. Growth is rapid throughout the summer months, and the first adults are ready to breed by late summer.

SPONGES

Furry Vase Sponge
Sycon ciliatum

ID FACT FILE

SIZE:
To 50 mm tall,
7.5 mm wide

DESCRIPTION:
Forming a
vase-like 'furry'
cylinder that
tapers towards
the top where a
fringe of stiff
spines forms a
collar around the
terminal opening;
colour pale
cream

HABITAT:
On rocks and
seaweeds on
lower shore

LOOKALIKES:
In *S. raphanus*
the form is more
spherical, arising
from a distinct
stalk, and the
collar longer and
more upright

To find this distinctive little sponge with its noticeably 'furry' surface you will need to peer up under dripping wet rock overhangs or search among clumps of large seaweeds when a spring tide has receded almost to its furthest point down the shore. On suitable shores this sponge can be very abundant, with clumps of individuals hanging up beneath the rocks. The best time to look is in spring, as this is an annual species that releases its larvae early in the year, after which the adults die off.

ANIMALS

J	F	M	A	M	J
J	A	S	O	N	D

Common Stalked Jellyfish
Haliclystus auricula

ID FACT FILE

SIZE:
To 4 cm long

DESCRIPTION:
Body green, brown or reddish, funnel-shaped with a stalk that embodies half the total height. Eight short arms, each surmounted by 100 tiny tentacles, form a star-like arrangement

HABITAT:
Rocky coasts, lower shore

LOOKALIKES:
There are several similar-looking species, but none nearly as common as this one

This small jellyfish is most likely to be found in a rock pool on the lower shore where it uses a sucker at the base of the stalk to attach itself to seaweeds and eelgrasses. In such a position it is in fact living upside down. It is not restricted to any one site as it can shift its position by performing cartwheels. The reproductive gonads are visible as strings along each of the arms. This species is common throughout the north Atlantic region.

CNIDARIANS

| J | F | M | A | M | J |
| J | A | S | O | N | D |

Sea Oak Hydroid

Dynamena pumila

ID FACT FILE

SIZE:
Up to 3 cm high

DESCRIPTION:
Forming stiff, whitish upright unbranched stems attached to large seaweeds. Each stem comprises a colony composed of numerous individuals

HABITAT:
Lower shore

LOOKALIKES:
Other hydroids are branched and mostly live offshore

Large, dull whitish colonies of this hydroid are a common sight waving gently in the water as the large seaweeds to which they are attached are gently swept to and fro by the waves. It usually attaches itself to the broad blades of kelps (*Laminaria* spp), Toothed Wrack, *Fucus serratus*, see page 24, and Bladder Wrack, *F. vesiculosus*, see page 22. Sometimes these can be almost covered with large colonies of this hydroid, although to see them at their best in water you must wade out a little way. Although common on northern European coasts, it is not found south of France's Atlantic coast.

CNIDARIANS

| J | F | M | A | M | J |
| J | A | S | O | N | D |

By-the-Wind Sailor
Velella velella

ID FACT FILE

Size:
3–5 cm long

Description:
Boat-shaped,
bright blue, with
numerous
individual polyps
projecting
beneath the
smooth upper
surface

Habitat:
Open oceans

Lookalikes:
None

Although this colonial hydroid spends its life
floating free in the wide expanses of the open
oceans, it is included here because after
summer or autumn storms it may be cast up on
our shores in countless millions. The animals
remain alive for a while after being stranded,
especially when they end up in rock pools, and
for a short time their striking blue colour can
be appreciated. However, they soon die and
decay, and then only the tough transparent
internal float and sail remain.

CNIDARIANS

Beadlet Anemone
Actinia equina

ID FACT FILE

SIZE:
To 5 cm high and broad

DESCRIPTION:
Colour deep bright red or brownish-red. When fully expanded in water the crown is covered in large numbers of fairly short and thick tentacles. Has a row of blue spots around the top of the column

HABITAT:
Common at all levels on rocky shores

LOOKALIKES:
See Strawberry Anemone, *A. fragacea*, opposite

The Beadlet Anemone is by far the commonest sea anemone on rocky shores throughout Europe, even being found in rock pools almost at the top of the shore. When the tide is out the anemone contracts into a jelly-like blob. During low tides in summertime exposed individuals are able to withstand many hours of drought and sun. The single ring of bright blue spots (acrorhagi) around the apex of the stem is very characteristic. Juveniles are disgorged by individuals of both sexes. As in most sea anemones, the tentacles are armed with stinging cells which kill prey, such as small fish. The tentacles then force the prey down into the 'mouth' in the centre of the disc.

CNIDARIANS

J	F	M	A	M	J
J	A	S	O	N	D

Strawberry Anemone
Actinia fragacea

ID FACT FILE

SIZE:
To 10 cm high

DESCRIPTION:
Colour deep
bright red, with a
strawberry-like
pale yellowish
mottling on the
sides of the
stem. Tentacles
numerous,
relatively short
and thick, blue
spots present on
stem

HABITAT:
On rocks on
lower shore

LOOKALIKES:
See Beadlet
Anemone,
A. equina,
opposite

This very attractive anemone was once
classified as a variety of the Beadlet Anemone,
A. equina, see opposite, but is now classed as a
separate species. It is much larger than the
Beadlet Anemone, and the 'strawberry' markings on the stem are distinctive. Unlike the
Beadlet Anemone, the Strawberry Anemone
almost always hangs downwards, rather than
being anchored in an upright position, making
it difficult to get a good view of the fully
expanded animal. It does not brood its young
and is not found higher than the lower shore.
Although as widely distributed as the Beadlet
Anemone, it is normally much scarcer.

CNIDARIANS

| J | F | M | A | M | J |
| J | A | S | O | N | D |

Snakelocks Anemone
Anemonia viridis

ID FACT FILE

SIZE:
Column to
5 cm wide,
4 cm high

DESCRIPTION:
Column rather
broad and squat.
Tentacles long
and waving, up to
200 in number,
not retractable.
Colour grey,
green or
brownish-red,
with purple-
tipped tentacles

HABITAT:
Rocky shores,
almost from top
to bottom if rock
pools present

LOOKALIKES:
None

This is a common anemone on most rocky shores and occurs in rock pools fairly high on the shore, often in rows along the cracks. Near the low water mark large individuals occur, which are capable of stinging and killing quite big fish. The variation in colour is mainly due to the presence of large numbers of microscopic algae (known as zooxanthellae) inside the tissues of the anemone, turning them green. This is why the Snakelocks Anemone always seeks the light and lives in well-illuminated rock pools. It is common on the south and west coasts of Britain and Ireland, and most European coasts except the southern North Sea.

CNIDARIANS

J	F	M	A	M	J
J	A	S	O	N	D

Gem Anemone
Bunodactis verrucosa

ID FACT FILE

SIZE:
To 8 cm high

DESCRIPTION:
Colour grey, speckled with white and with a green central disc. Tentacles in cycles of 6, with a maximum total of 48

HABITAT:
Lower shore, on rocks

LOOKALIKES:
Dahlia Anemone, *Urticina felina*, see page 108, is larger, up to 20 cm across the fully expanded tentacles, which reach a maximum of 160 in number

It is the pearly white gem-like flecks, contrasting brightly against the greyish background of the tentacles that give this anemone its common name. The fairly long column is usually retracted into a crevice in the rocks, leaving only the tentacles visible. Sometimes small clusters of individuals can be found at the bottom of a rock pool, although care is needed as they will quickly retract their tentacles to avoid being spotted. Like many anemones, the Gem can reproduce asexually through a process of 'budding' or 'fission'. The Gem Anemone is found on the south and west coasts of the British Isles, southwards to the Mediterranean.

CNIDARIANS

Dahlia Anemone

Urticina felina

J	F	M	A	M	J
J	A	S	O	N	D

ID FACT FILE

SIZE:
To 10 cm across

DESCRIPTION:
A broad, squat anemone, always with debris adhering to the outer surface of the column. Tentacles up to 160, arranged in multiples of ten. Colour variable

HABITAT:
In pools and under stones on the lower shore and in the sublittoral zone

LOOKALIKES:
See Gem Anemone, *Bunodactis verrucosa*, page 107

The discovery of a pool containing large numbers of this superb and widespread anemone is a major event when rock pooling on the shore, although not a common one. It is more usual to come across small, rather drab singletons beneath stones. The colour is very variable, and the form illustrated is probably the most attractive. This specimen was in one of a series of small pools which held nearly one hundred Dahlia Anemones, ranging from greyish to brilliant magenta, some very large. Yet without lifting aside the great tangles of brown seaweeds, none would have been visible.

CNIDARIANS

J	F	M	A	M	J
J	A	S	O	N	D

Trumpet Anemone
Aiptasia mutabilis

ID FACT FILE

SIZE:
To 12 cm high

DESCRIPTION:
Column tall and slender, flaring outwards just beneath the tentacles, which can be retracted only slowly and partially. Colour brown, bluish on the disk

HABITAT:
Lower shore on rocky coasts

LOOKALIKES:
None

Although the maximum height of the column can be as much as 12 cm, those found on the accessible part of the shore at low spring tides are usually much smaller. The way that the slender column flares suddenly outwards just beneath the rows of rather short tentacles is very distinctive, as is the overall brown coloration with the attractive blue tints on the disc. The Trumpet Anemone is most often found by turning over rocks, but can also be seen in pools at low tide. It occurs from southwest England southwards to the Mediterranean, and can be very common where it occurs, as on some Cornish shores.

J	F	M	A	M	J
J	A	S	O	N	D

Daisy Anemone
Cereus pedunculatus

ID FACT FILE

SIZE:
Disc up to
12 cm across

DESCRIPTION:
Column tall and
trumpet-like, with
a broad, mottled
disc with
500–1000
strongly
patterned
tentacles

HABITAT:
Rocky coasts,
middle and lower
shore, in pools

LOOKALIKES:
*Sagartia
troglodytes*,
found in similar
habitats, has up
to 200 tentacles
only, with more
pronounced
black and white
markings

This fairly large anemone is most likely to be
found jammed into a narrow crevice in a rock
pool, with just the broad mass of tentacles
protruding. Any slight disturbance will cause
these to be retracted, but they reappear again
after just a few minutes. Daisy Anemones can
also be found on sandy shores, with just the
tentacles visible at the surface, the rest of the
body being buried in the sand but always
firmly anchored to a stone or rock beneath.
This widespread but seldom abundant
anemone is found on the south and west
coasts of Britain and Ireland, southwards to
the Mediterranean.

CNIDARIANS

| J | F | M | A | M | J |
| J | A | S | O | N | D |

A Sea Anemone

Sagartiogeton undatus

ID FACT FILE

SIZE:
To 12 cm high,
2 cm across

DESCRIPTION:
Column tall, with
a series of
vertical grooves,
pale brownish.
Tentacles up to
200, long,
hanging down
around the
column, white
with long dark
stripes

HABITAT:
In pools and
crevices on
lower shore

LOOKALIKES:
In *Sagartia
elegans*
tentacles are
fewer and
shorter, colour
more
variable

Although most often found in pools or wedged into crevices on rocky shores, this widespread anemone also lives attached to deeply buried stones on sandy shores, with just the top of the column and tentacles protruding from the sand. Unfortunately this species is most often seen as a blob of shapeless jelly hanging from a rock face at low tide, but a careful search may reveal the odd specimen lurking in a pool, as in the illustration, when the full beauty of the mass of long tentacles can be appreciated.

J	F	M	A	M	J
J	A	S	O	N	D

Bootlace Worm

Lineus longissimus

ID FACT FILE

SIZE:
10 m long

DESCRIPTION:
Body very long
and slender,
dark brown to
black with an
iridescent sheen.
Head with a
square 'snout'
and with 10–20
indistinct eyes
on either side

HABITAT:
In crevices and
under stones on
rocky shores

LOOKALIKES:
*Tubulanus
annulatus* is only
up to 75 cm long
and has a
whitish pattern
against the
blackish body, a
broad, rounded
head and no
visible eyes. It is
found under
stones or in
sand and mud

Although found widely on the shores of the
Atlantic and North Sea, the Bootlace Worm is
seldom if ever abundant, and usually just crops
up as the odd individual discovered by turning
over a rock on the lower shore. Although 10 m
is quite a common length, specimens up to
30 m long have been found. The length is not
very obvious as the worm normally coils itself
into an untidy knot. The ribbon worms
(Phylum Nemertea) to which this species
belongs are active hunters, using a large
proboscis (sometimes tipped with poison) to
capture their prey.

J	F	M	A	M	J
J	A	S	O	N	D

Estuary Ragworm
Nereis diversicolor

ID FACT FILE

SIZE:
6–12 cm long

DESCRIPTION:
Body long and flattened, rather limp, composed of 100 or more similar segments. Colour variable, yellowish, orange or greenish, but always with a conspicuous red blood vessel running down the centre of the back

HABITAT:
In muddy sand of estuaries

LOOKALIKES:
Several other similar-looking ragworms are widespread

This species, found throughout Europe, normally lies concealed within a burrow in muddy sand in estuaries and sheltered inlets, but it may sometimes be found by turning over rocks when these lie on a suitable substrate. Ragworms belong to the family Nereidae, all of which are active hunters of other small animals. On the head there is a pair of conspicuous palps, while the four eyes are placed more or less in a square. When being handled ragworms can give a painful bite, using a large proboscis furnished with jaw-like teeth. They are often used as bait by anglers.

Greenleaf Worm
Eulalia viridis

ID FACT FILE

SIZE:
5–15 cm long

DESCRIPTION:
Body bright leaf-green to dark bluish-green, sometimes with black markings along the back. Head with a pair of antennae on either side and a fifth in the centre between the pair of small black eyes. Paddles slender, pointed

HABITAT:
Lower shore, on rocks

LOOKALIKES:
E. bilineata is paler, with two blackish lines down the middle of the back and oval paddles. *Phyllodoce lamelligera* is much larger (6–60 cm) with 4 pairs of thin tentacles on head

Like all paddleworms (family Phyllodocidae) the Greenleaf Worm is an active predator, killing its prey with an amazingly large proboscis which can be projected in front of the head. Down each side of the body is a row of numerous leg-like paddles that are used both for walking on rock and swimming in water. Mucous is secreted in response to rough handling. Although odd individuals of this very widespread worm may be found by turning over rocks, at other times hundreds or even thousands may be seen swarming across the rocks at low tide. Next day there may be none.

J	F	M	A	M	J
J	A	S	O	N	D

Long-tailed Scale Worm
Lagisca extenuata

ID FACT FILE

SIZE:
3–4 cm long

DESCRIPTION:
Body clad with 15 pairs of oval scales, almost parallel-sided at first, but then tapering off abruptly at the rear to form a little 'tail' which is bare of scales

HABITAT:
Under stones on the lower shore

LOOKALIKES:
Several similar-looking scale worms occur under stones on the lower shore, but they lack the 'tail' seen in this species

In life the tail is often withdrawn somewhat up into the body, as depicted in the illustration, in which the scaleless nature of the shortened and compressed tail is clearly visible. This species is quite common under stones on the lower shore throughout the whole of Europe, rapidly moving across the wet surface of the stone as soon as it is uncovered. Each of the individual scales is warty with a long fringe around the margin and a pale central spot.

WORMS

J	F	M	A	M	J
J	A	S	O	N	D

Twin-spiral Fanworm

Bispira volutacornis

ID FACT FILE

SIZE:
Body up to 10 cm long; fan about 1.5 cm across

DESCRIPTION:
Body long, stout brownish, surmounted by a pair of extensible fans made up of some 200 interlocking brownish tentacles with whitish tips, mounted in twin whorls

HABITAT:
Rock crevices in pools at low water on the lower shore

LOOKALIKES:
Most other fanworms have single fans with fewer tentacles in a single row

Unless you dig them out you will never see the body of a fanworm (family Sabellidae) as it is hidden in a crevice between rocks or deep in sand or mud. The body is enclosed within a mucous tube, often reinforced with sand particles, forming a tough but flexible jacket. The worm feeds and breathes by extruding one or more fan-like sets of tentacles from the mouth of the tube. These act as a large gill, enabling the worm to survive in its stagnant burrow, and also filter particles of food out of the water. This species is very widespread in Europe, but restricted to southwestern coasts in the British Isles.

Sentinel Fanworm
Megalomma vesiculosum

ID FACT FILE

SIZE:
Body up to
12 cm long; fan
about 1.5–2 cm
across

DESCRIPTION:
Body reddish or
purplish, spotted
with white.
Tentacles about
50, rather broad
and short,
yellowish-brown,
each with a
prominent dark
eyespot near the
outer tip

HABITAT:
In sandy-
bottomed rock
pools on lower
shore

LOOKALIKES:
Several other
fanworms are
similar.
Peacock Worm,
Sabella pavonina
has more (about
100) and longer
tentacles

Broad, shallow rock pools with a bottom of
sand or fine gravel will often have lots of little
stony tubes projecting upwards for about
2–3 cm. If you sit quite still you will see
little fans gradually beginning to expand from
these tubes, which belong to the Sentinel
Fanworm. The need to remain motionless is
due to the eyespots on the tentacles. These are
present in many fanworms, but seem
particularly acute in this species, which pulls
instantly back into its tube at any sign of
movement nearby. Its British distribution just
includes the southwest, but it is more
widespread in Europe.

WORMS

J	F	M	A	M	J
J	A	S	O	N	D

Keelworm
Pomatoceros lamarcki

ID FACT FILE

SIZE:
Up to 2.5 cm long

DESCRIPTION:
Body variously coloured. Tube sinuous, hard and white, with a prominent ridge along the back and a less prominent one on either side

HABITAT:
On rocks on middle and lower shore

LOOKALIKES:
P. triqueter is mainly found below tidemarks and has just a single ridge on its tube

When turning over rocks on the shores anywhere in northern Europe to see what exciting animals are concealed beneath (most of which you will find in this book), you may often find it useful to wear gloves. This is because your hands can easily become covered in tiny lacerations from the hard, sharp-edged tubes of this worm, a member of the tubeworm family, Serpulidae. These often cover the undersides of rocks in an interconnecting maze, but you are unlikely to see the occupants poke their heads out with a small fan of tentacles to feed. This only happens when the tubes are submerged.

J	F	M	A	M	J
J	A	S	O	N	D

Red-fanned Tubeworm
Serpula vermicularis

ID FACT FILE

SIZE:
Body 5–7 cm;
fan about 5–10
mm across

DESCRIPTION:
Body long and
slender,
composed of
some 200
segments, yellow
or red. Tube
hard, pinkish-
white or pink,
about 5 mm in
diameter. Fan
of tentacles
bright red

HABITAT:
On rocks on
lower shore

LOOKALIKES:
None

In this cosmopolitan species the distinctive pinkish tube is often only anchored near its base, leaving the rest floating free in the water. Sometimes whole groups of tubes are found together, twisting around one another to form an untidy mass. At intervals along each tube there is a recessed ring, and several rows of saw-toothed ridges run lengthwise along the surface. Allied to the colour, this makes them recognisable even when the fan of crimson tentacles is not protruding. As in all tubeworms, one of these tentacles is modified to form a plug (operculum) for the tube.

J	F	M	A	M	J
J	A	S	O	N	D

Calcareous Tube Worm

Spirorbis spirorbis

ID FACT FILE

SIZE:
Coil 3–4 mm
across

DESCRIPTION:
Tube smooth and
white, coiled
clockwise, with a
prominent 'skirt'
around the lower
margin which
connects to the
substrate

HABITAT:
On large
seaweeds

LOOKALIKES:
Tubes of
S. tridentatus are
attached to
shells and rocks
and have three
rounded ridges
along the spiral.
S. rupestris lives
among red
encrusting algae
(see page 32)
and the end of
its tube is often
raised upwards

The tightly coiled spiral white tubes of this
worm, common on all northern European
coasts, could easily be mistaken for the shells
of miniature molluscs. They are attached in
large numbers to the broad fronds of
seaweeds, mostly Toothed Wrack, *Fucus
serratus*, see page 24, but also to kelps. When
the tide is in the worm protrudes a small fan of
almost transparent tentacles from the mouth
of the tube to feed. This species constructs
its tube in an anti-clockwise spiral (illustration
is shown from below), and this is as invariable
as in some other species which use a clockwise
spiral.

WORMS

J	F	M	A	M	J
J	A	S	O	N	D

Blow Lug
Arenicola marina

ID FACT FILE

SIZE:
12–25 cm

DESCRIPTION:
Body brownish-red, with a stoutly built front half furnished with shorter red gill-tufts on the rearmost 13 segments, then a long, narrower 'tail' portion lacking gills

HABITAT:
Sandy shores

LOOKALIKES:
A. defodiens is almost black. In *Arenicolides branchialis* there is no narrower 'tail' portion and brownish gill-tufts are present throughout

The Blow Lug, often just called the Lugworm because it is so common and the only member of the lugworm family (Arenicolidae) familiar to most people, is common on sandy shores throughout Europe. Unless you dig for it (as many anglers do for bait) you will not see the worm itself, which lives in a U-shaped burrow beneath the sand. What you will see is thousands of its characteristic and rather neatly coiled casts (see illustration), comprised of sand passed out of the worm's rear end after any food has been separated from it. A short way from the cast is a small depression, the 'blow-hole', marking where the worm's mouth lies as it sucks in the sand.

WORMS

A Bristleworm

Amphitritides gracilis

ID FACT FILE

SIZE:
Up to 12 cm long

DESCRIPTION:
Body soft and
rather fragile,
reddish-brown,
fairly stout at
front, tapering
gradually towards
rear end. Head
with numerous
slender, whitish
feeding tentacles
and two pairs of
bushy, reddish
gills

HABITAT:
Lower shore,
under stones

LOOKALIKES:
*Neoamphitrite
figulus* has three
pairs of bushy
gills and is up to
25 cm long

This rather fragile worm lives in a slightly
scrappy tube composed of sand grains in a
loose matrix of mucous secreted by the worm
and attached to the buried underside of a rock
or shell. When the rock is lifted the tube may
be torn free, leaving the worm fully exposed,
as seen in the illustration which also shows
the coiled body, characteristic of this species
when free of its gallery. This can easily be
reconstructed by the worm later, once the rock
has been carefully replaced without crushing
the worm.

WORMS

J	F	M	A	M	J
J	A	S	O	N	D

Sand Mason Worm

Lanice conchilega

ID FACT FILE

SIZE:
Up to 30 cm long

DESCRIPTION:
Body yellowish-pink or brown. Front part of body consists of 17 segments, surmounted by two pairs of bushy gills, of which the first pair sit on much longer stalks

HABITAT:
On sandy and sand/mud shores

LOOKALIKES:
None

As with the Blow Lug, *Arenicola marina*, see page 121, it is not the worm itself that you will see which lives below the sand or in a mixture of sand and mud, but the material consequence of its invisible presence as revealed on the surface. This comprises a rather tatty-looking turret built by the worm and extending upwards for about 2.5 cm above the surface of the sand. These structures are built of sand grains cemented together with mucous and topped with a rather untidy 'mop-like' series of sinuous strands. These miniature turrets often occur in thousands on flat shores, but can also be found in rock pools with sandy bottoms, over most of northwest Europe.

Honeycomb Worm
Sabellaria alveolata

J	F	M	A	M	J
J	A	S	O	N	D

ID FACT FILE

SIZE:
3–4 cm long

DESCRIPTION:
Head with a circular crown of spines. Many feeding tentacles around the mouth. Long tube-like 'tail' turned forwards along the underside. Tubes forming large masses.

HABITAT:
Lower shore

LOOKALIKES:
None

Another name for this species is the Reef-building Worm, derived from its habit of constructing its tube in large colonies which in some areas are so vast that they form reef-like structures. These are attached to rocks on the lower shore, and are better developed on exposed, wave-pounded shores than on more sheltered ones. The individual tubes are composed of sand grains fixed together with an extremely powerful cement secreted by the occupant, hence the tube's ability to withstand the pressure from winter storms. This species is found in southwest Britain and around most European coasts.

CRUSTACEANS

Common Acorn Barnacle
Semibalanus balanoides

J	F	M	A	M	J
J	A	S	O	N	D

ID FACT FILE

SIZE:
Up to 1 cm
across

DESCRIPTION:
Shape broadly
conical to fairly
columnar. Colour
white. Aperture
diamond-shaped,
composed of 4
plates two of
which are much
larger than the
others and sur-
rounded by six
much larger,
grooved plates

HABITAT:
Middle shore,
on rocks

LOOKALIKES:
See Dark Acorn
Barnacle

This very common species, found on all
European coasts, often occurs in countless
millions on rocky shores where it tends to
occur lower down the shore. Barnacles have
quite sharply angled edges and can make
walking across rocks barefoot quite
uncomfortable. Eggs are brooded inside the
adult and then released as free-living larvae
into the water. These larvae feed up among the
plankton before moulting into a simple shelled
stage that eventually settles down on a rock and
becomes the barnacle we see on the shore.

CRUSTACEANS

J	F	M	A	M	J
J	A	S	O	N	D

Dark Acorn Barnacle

Balanus perforatus

ID FACT FILE

Size:
To 3 cm across
at base

Description:
A dirty greyish-
black barnacle
with its small
oval aperture
deeply sunk
within the
summit of the
volcano-shaped
strongly-grooved
outer plates

Habitat:
On rocks on
middle and lower
shore

Lookalikes:
B. crenatus is
white with
smooth wall
plates. See also
Common Acorn
Barnacle

This barnacle can hardly be mistaken for any
other on account of its large size, dark colour
and volcano-like shape. It often occurs in large
numbers on rocks lower down the shore, but
seldom forms the kind of overwhelming carpet
seen in the smaller and commoner species. It
breeds during summertime, and the larvae
eventually settle on rocks in August and
September. The similarly large, but smooth
and white *B. crenatus* breeds in winter, and is
restricted to the lower shore only. *B perforatus*
is a southern species, absent from northern
Britain and the North Sea coast of Europe.

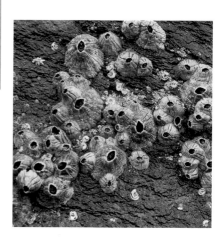

CRUSTACEANS

| J | F | M | A | M | J |
| J | A | S | O | N | D |

Common Goose Barnacle
Lepas anatifera

ID FACT FILE

SIZE:
'Shell' 5 cm long

DESCRIPTION:
Plates smooth
and white,
suspended at
the tip of a long,
slender, blackish
'stalk' or
peduncle.
Attached to
flotsam usually
in dense masses

HABITAT:
Oceanic, often
cast up on the
shore

LOOKALIKES:
Buoy Barnacle
(see text)

Pieces of wood cast up on the shore are
often covered in a mass of Common Goose
Barnacles, although by the time you find them
they will all be dead and will probably be
starting to smell a little. Each barnacle consists
of a total of just five broad, smooth white
plates, hanging from the tip of a long blackish,
rubbery stalk that is attached to the wood or
other material that is being used as a float. In
the Buoy Barnacle, *Dosima fascicularis*, the
stalk is very short and grey rather than black,
and is attached to a white polystyrene-like float
secreted by the barnacles themselves. Both
species are often cast up around the coasts
of Europe.

CRUSTACEANS

Pill Isopod
Sphaeroma serratum

ID FACT FILE

SIZE:
To 11 mm long

DESCRIPTION:
Body broad and oval, like a pill millipede or woodlouse, made up of numerous segments, pale pinkish-white with brownish-orange bands along the margins of the segments

HABITAT:
Middle to lower shore, under rocks

LOOKALIKES:
There are several similar species difficult to tell apart but usually less common or in non-rocky habitats. (See text)

'Family groups' containing several males, females and juveniles of various ages are often found under stones or in crevices among rocks. Like pill millipedes and some woodlice, they can roll themselves up into a perfect ball, protected all-over by their shiny, armoured plates. *Dynamene bidentata* looks very similar, lives in similar habitats but is smaller (to 7 mm long) and has a less oval outline, having straighter sides. In both species the males are larger than the females, with a range that includes the south and west coasts of Britain southwards to the Mediterranean.

CRUSTACEANS

Sea Slater
Ligia oceanica

ID FACT FILE

SIZE:
Up to 3 cm long

DESCRIPTION:
Body elongated oval, flattened, yellowish or brownish, consisting of numerous distinct segments, narrower at the rear and with two 'tails' and a pair of long antennae on the head

HABITAT:
Upper shore

LOOKALIKES:
None

Sea Slaters are large isopods and are seldom seen in daytime unless disturbed from their hiding places in a crevice or beneath a stone. They emerge at night or sometimes in cool, dull weather to scuttle around across damp rocks on the upper shore in search of food. Sea Slaters only inhabit the very uppermost zone of the shore where the tides do not normally reach. Although living for a total of three years, reproduction only takes place once, in the third year, and mating pairs are often observed.

J	F	M	A	M	J
J	A	S	O	N	D

Isopod
Idotea baltica

ID FACT FILE

SIZE:
Male to 3 cm
long

DESCRIPTION:
Body often
attractively pat-
terned in black
and silverygrey,
relatively long
and narrow,
tapering at both
ends. Head
with a pair of
antennae about
one-third the
length of the
body

HABITAT:
Lowest part of
shore exposed at
spring tides

LOOKALIKES:
Several similar
species occur
but always with-
out the whitish
markings

This species, common on all coasts, is the most
attractive of several small isopods found in
pools, under stones and among seaweeds on
the lower shore, where they are only exposed
during spring tides. The white markings on the
body, when present, are characteristic, and
contrast with the much darker ground colour
which varies from green to brown or blackish.
In these small isopod crustaceans the shape of
the hindmost segment, the telson, is important
in identification. In this species it tapers
towards a squared-off end with a bulge in the
centre.

J	F	M	A	M	J
J	A	S	O	N	D

Lance-tailed Isopod
Synisoma lancifer

ID FACT FILE

SIZE:
To 2.5 cm long

DESCRIPTION:
Body long and narrow, parallel-sided, reddish-brown, with seven broadly rounded segments tipped by a much narrower lance-shaped telson. Antennae nearly half length of body

HABITAT:
Lower shore

LOOKALIKES:
The body of S. *acuminatum* is narrower and of the same width as the telson

This very narrow-bodied, reddish species is very difficult to spot when it is resting on kelps and other seaweeds towards the low-water mark. In fact you are very unlikely to notice it unless it gives away its position by moving. The similar but narrower S. *acuminatum* is often found in rock pools, especially on the Sea Oak, *Halidrys siliquosa*, see page 26, on which it is nearly invisible as it closely matches the long, narrow air bladders.

CRUSTACEANS

J	F	M	A	M	J
J	A	S	O	N	D

Common Sandhopper
Talitrus saltator

ID FACT FILE

SIZE:
To 2.5 cm long

DESCRIPTION:
Body flattened
from side to
side, shining
greyish-
transparent.
Legs numerous,
none enlarged to
any great extent.
Second pair of
antennae long
and slender

HABITAT:
Sandy shores

LOOKALIKES:
Many similar
species, most of
which have at
least one pair
of modified,
thickened legs

Sandhoppers belong to the order Amphipoda,
characterised by the distinct side-to-side
flattening of the body. When on land this
obliges them to lie on their sides rather than
standing fully upright on their legs. The
Common Sandhopper can often be found in
great numbers on all the coasts of Europe
simply by lifting up a mass of beached seaweed
or a large flat stone on the upper part of a
sandy shore, above the reach of normal high
tides. As soon as they are exposed dozens of
sandhoppers will either hop away or burrow
into the sand.

CRUSTACEANS

| J | F | M | A | M | J |
| J | A | S | O | N | D |

Common Prawn
Palaemon serratus

ID FACT FILE

SIZE:
To 11 cm long

DESCRIPTION:
Body slightly
flattened from
side to side, pale
translucent
brownish,
banded darker.
Long, upwardly
curved pointed,
heavily toothed
rostrum jutting
out from between
the eyes. Two
pairs of
antennae, one
pair long and
whip-like

HABITAT:
Pools on rocky
coasts

LOOKALIKES:
P. elegans is
smaller (to
63 mm), has
less upturned
rostrum with only
very small teeth
on it. See also
Brown Shrimp,
*Crangon,
crangon*,
page 134

This is the largest of the intertidal prawns and
by far the most common, being found in rock
pools all up the shore around the coasts of
Europe. Really large adults are seldom seen,
but medium-sized specimens are common, and
large numbers of almost transparent-bodied
juveniles are usually present, often in small
groups hanging motionless in the water, when
they are almost invisible. Apart from their
smaller size, the juveniles are much like the
adults. Along with crabs, prawns are included
in the very large order Decapoda.

CRUSTACEANS

| J | F | M | A | M | J |
| J | A | S | O | N | D |

Brown or Edible Shrimp

Crangon crangon

ID FACT FILE

SIZE:
Up to 9 cm long

DESCRIPTION:
Body slightly
flattened from
top to bottom,
pale speckled
brown. Rostrum
smooth and
tapered, with
a rounded tip.
Two pairs of
antennae, one
pair long and
whip-like

HABITAT:
Lower shore,
on muddy sand
and gravel

LOOKALIKES:
See Common
Prawn, *Palaemon
serratus*,
page 133

Whereas the Common Prawn, *Palaemon
serratus*, see page 133, is most likely to be
found in rock pools, the Brown Shrimp is
commoner on shores of muddy sand or gravel,
but is also present in rock pools which have
this kind of bottom. The Brown Shrimp is far
less transparent than the Common Prawn, and
its body is slightly flattened from top to bottom
rather than from side to side. The most
obvious difference is the absence of any long,
pointed, heavily toothed upturned rostrum
projecting forwards from between the eyes in
the Brown Shrimp. Common on all European
coasts, it is an important commercial species.

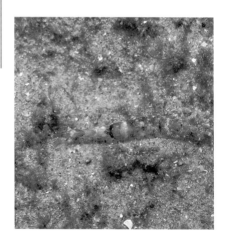

CRUSTACEANS

Hooded Shrimp
Athanas nitescens

J	F	M	A	M	J
J	A	S	O	N	D

ID FACT FILE

SIZE:
Up to 2 cm long

DESCRIPTION:
Body dark
brownish-red,
green or blue,
with a pale
pinkish-white
stripe down the
middle of the
back. Front legs
greatly thickened

HABITAT:
Lower shore,
under rocks and
seaweed

LOOKALIKES:
None

This small but attractive species, which with its
enlarged 'claws' rather resembles a miniature
lobster, is found all along the coasts of Europe.
As in all prawns, a quick flick of its flap-like tail
will result in a rapid retreat backwards out of
trouble. When the tide is out it seeks shelter
in the cool, damp environment beneath rocks
and large seaweeds. As in all prawns, females
may sometimes be found carrying a mass of
eggs beneath them, when they are said to be
'in berry'.

CRUSTACEANS

Chamaeleon Prawn

Hippolyte varians

ID FACT FILE

SIZE:
Up to 32 mm
long

DESCRIPTION:
Colour variable:
green, brown or
red. Body rather
long and narrow,
not very deep.
Rostrum deep,
with just a
solitary tooth set
just before the
eye-socket

HABITAT:
Lower shore,
among seaweeds

LOOKALIKES:
H. inermis is up
to 42 mm long
and has a long
projecting
rostrum. *H.
longirostris* is
only 20 mm long

This small prawn bears pigment cells that
contain three colours: red, yellow or blue.
The proportion of each of these visible
throughout the body can be varied by the
shrimp depending on the colour of the
background on which it is sitting. The colour
of the background is detected by the eyes,
which send nerve impulses down to the glands
that regulate colour change. This is a slow
process, taking about a week, but allows the
prawn to remain camouflaged among seaweeds
of various colours.

CRUSTACEANS

| J | F | M | A | M | J |
| J | A | S | O | N | D |

Common Hermit Crab

Pagurus bernhardus

ID FACT FILE

SIZE:
Carapace to
3.5 cm long

DESCRIPTION:
Body tapering
and twisting
towards rear,
enabling it to fit
within the empty
shell of a
periwinkle or
other mollusc.
Rostrum sharply
pointed. Thick
eyestalks much
shorter than first
pair (of short)
antenna. No
bristles on large
right-hand 'claw'

HABITAT:
Middle and lower
shore

LOOKALIKES:
P. cuanensis is
smaller
(carapace to 16
mm long). Large
'claws' covered
with bristles

Hermit crabs are unusual in lacking the broad, armoured bodies seen in other crabs. Instead the long, slender body is soft and pliant, with a sideways spiral that enables it to fit inside a coiled shell like a finger in a glove. The empty shells of various molluscs are used, and the crab has to make a swift change from one to another when it requires a larger home as it grows out of its old one. In late summer the shell may be covered with a pink mat of the Colonial Hydroid, *Hydractinia echinata,* which is found only on shells occupied by hermit crabs. The Common Hermit Crab is found along all European coasts southwards to Portugal.

CRUSTACEANS

| J | F | M | A | M | J |
| J | A | S | O | N | D |

Common Squat Lobster
Galathea squamifera

ID FACT FILE

SIZE:
Body up to
3.5 cm long

DESCRIPTION:
Colour brown,
often with a
greenish tint,
body oval,
rostrum short
and broad, spiny.
Claws not spiny,
lower
articulations
(nearest the
body) with
strong, curved
spines

HABITAT:
Lower shore,
under rocks and
in rock crevices

LOOKALIKES:
G. strigosa, bright
red with blue
bands, is much
bigger, to
9 cm body length

Of the two squat lobsters likely to be found between tidemarks, this is by far the most common, and on some shores (e.g. in Cornwall) can be extremely abundant under rocks on the lower shore. As in all squat lobsters, the body is rather flattened from top to bottom, enabling it to slide easily into rock crevices and beneath large stones at low tide. The abdomen is flexed upwards and inwards underneath the thorax, giving a rather squat outline, hence the common name. This widespread species is found around the coasts of Europe.

CRUSTACEANS

Broad-clawed Porcelain Crab

Porcellana platycheles

J	F	M	A	M	J
J	A	S	O	N	D

ID FACT FILE

SIZE:
Up to 1.5 cm long

DESCRIPTION:
Body almost circular, flattened, dull brown, with a fringe of long hairs around the margins. Claws very large and flat, also fringed with long hairs. Antennae very long and whip-like

HABITAT:
Under rocks on lower shore

LOOKALIKES:
Hairy crab, *Pilumnus hirtellus*, page 148, is hairy but only has small claws

If you carefully turn over a large stone on the lower shore you may find as many as a dozen or more of these large-clawed, densely hairy little crabs (it is also called the Hairy Porcelain Crab) clinging to the underside. Some of these will immediately plop into the water, while others will sidle around on the rock, trailing their long hair fringes across its wet surface. In spring and summer you may find females carrying their eggs fixed firmly in place beneath their body. This very common crab occurs everywhere along the rocky coasts of Europe.

CRUSTACEANS

Long-clawed Porcelain Crab

Porcellana longicornis

J	F	M	A	M	J
J	A	S	O	N	D

ID FACT FILE

SIZE:
To 1 cm long

DESCRIPTION:
Body almost circular, colour variable, from grey to brown, to olive green. Claws quite long and slender. Whole animal shiny and hairless. Antennae long and whip-like

HABITAT:
Under rocks and on coarse gravel on lower shore

LOOKALIKES:
None

As soon as you expose it by lifting a rock this small, rather delicately built crab will quickly start running, holding its long, slender claws out in front in a very characteristic way. With its smooth body and general appearance, plus small size, it can hardly be mistaken for any other crabs found on the shore. It is never as common under stones as the Broad-Clawed Porcelain Crab, *P. platycheles*, see page 139, usually occurring as singletons. In deeper water it is more often found among colonies of bryozoans and hydroids. Distribution includes all European coasts.

CRUSTACEANS

Lesser Spider Crab
Hyas coarctatus

ID FACT FILE

SIZE:
To 5 cm long

DESCRIPTION:
Body
pear-shaped,
broader at the
back, brownish-
red. Claws
(chelipeds)
almost as long
as first pair of
walking legs,
all of which are
very slender.
Antennae short,
spine-like

HABITAT:
Lower shore,
under rocks and
in rock pools

LOOKALIKES:
Great Spider
Crab, *H. araneus*
is larger (to
105 mm long),
darker brown and
chelipeds much
shorter than first
pair of walking
legs. See also
other spider
crabs

It is the long, slender legs that give spider
crabs their common name. Most species tend
to camouflage their bodies and claws with bits
of sponge, hydroid or (as illustrated below)
small bits of seaweeds. Spider crabs feed on
very small items of food, so they only need
relatively small, weak pincers. This species is
found in rock pools among seaweeds and
beneath rocks on the lower shore. It is
common all round the coasts of Europe,
although often rather rare between tidemarks.

CRUSTACEANS

Scorpion Spider Crab
Inachus dorsettensis

J	F	M	A	M	J
J	A	S	O	N	D

ID FACT FILE

SIZE:
To 3 cm long

DESCRIPTION:
Body
pear-shaped,
broader than
long, brownish-
orange. Rostrum
short, with two
rather blunt
horns. Sharp
spine present
behind each
eye. Claws
(chelipeds)
rather short,
front pair of
legs (pereopods)
very long

HABITAT:
Lower shore,
under rocks

LOOKALIKES:
I. thoracicus and
I. phalangium are
similar but less
likely to be found
on the shore
even on very low
tides

This crab is only likely to be found on the
lowest part of the shore that will be uncovered
by unusually low spring tides. As these also
expose many other creatures that are never
normally seen, it is worth making an effort to
get to the shore on those days. This species
usually covers most of its legs and body with
bits of living sponge, making it impossible to
see structural details and rendering the crab
almost invisible until it moves. Its eyes are
mounted on long retractile stalks. This is a
widespread spider crab, found all round the
coasts of Europe.

J	F	M	A	M	J
J	A	S	O	N	D

CRUSTACEANS

Long-legged Spider Crab
Macropodia rostrata

ID FACT FILE

SIZE:
Carapace up to 22 mm long

DESCRIPTION:
Carapace rather triangular in outline, almost covered with large tubercles, three of which form a triangle at the front, with one at the rear and two smaller ones on either side. Rostrum long and slightly blunt-tipped. Legs very long and spindly. Claws (chelipeds) short and slender

HABITAT:
Lower shore, on rocks, sand and mud

LOOKALIKES:
In *M. tenuirostris* there is only one smaller tubercle on either side of the carapace; rostrum long and pointed

This is a very gangly looking spider crab, quite different from the preceding two species. It normally camouflages itself with numerous small pieces of red seaweed. It is only likely to be seen during extremely low tides when the lowest part of the shore is exposed for a short period. It can be found by turning over stones, but may also be noticed scampering across the bare sand or mud on its long legs, when it looks like a piece of animated cast-up seaweed. It also swims well, paddling vigorously with its long legs. It is widespread on all coasts.

CRUSTACEANS

J	F	M	A	M	J
J	A	S	O	N	D

Edible Crab
Cancer pagurus

ID FACT FILE

SIZE:
Carapace up to
25 cm broad

DESCRIPTION:
Carapace heavy,
squat, oval,
smooth-topped,
brownish-red,
with a margin
that is crimped
like a piecrust.
Claws (chelae)
large, massively
built, with black
tips

HABITAT:
Lower shore of
rocky coasts

LOOKALIKES:
None

This very distinctive crab, found on all shores,
is easily recognised, especially by anyone who
has ever ordered a complete one in a
restaurant. The largest (and very valuable)
individuals, weighing several kilograms, are
found in deeper water offshore, the average
size of the juvenile specimens which can be
found abundantly beneath stones on the lower
shore usually being about 5–10 cm across.
Females come inshore in late spring in order
to moult their skins and mate. In late summer
they migrate back into deeper water, delaying
egg-laying until quite late in the winter.

Masked Crab
Corystes cassivelaunus

ID FACT FILE

SIZE:
Carapace up to
4 cm long

DESCRIPTION:
Carapace a
rather elongated
oval, pale brown,
sparsely
furrowed.
Antennae long
and stout,
covered in
bristles and
forming a tube.
Male claws
(chelipeds)
are very long

HABITAT:
In sand on lower
shore

LOOKALIKES:
None

The Masked Crab lives buried in sand on the lower shore of all European coasts, but can occasionally be found sitting on the surface at low tide. It cannot be mistaken for anything else because of its unique long, spine-like bristly antennae. These form a tube whose tip is protruded through the surface of the sand, enabling the crab to breathe. In males the claws (chelipeds) are twice as long as the carapace and held out in front. In females the chelipeds are much shorter. Food consists of small sand-living invertebrates.

CRUSTACEANS

J	F	M	A	M	J
J	A	S	O	N	D

Velvet Swimming Crab
Necora puber

ID FACT FILE

Size:
Carapace to
6.5 cm long and
broad

Description:
Carapace wider
at the front than
at the rear, dark
brown or
greenish-brown,
smooth and
velvety, only
slightly convex.
Five sharp teeth
on either side of
the eyes, which
are red. Rear
legs flattened

Habitat:
Under rocks on
the lower shore

Lookalikes:
See other crabs

The Velvet Swimming Crab is usually common
under stones and rocks on the lower shore on
all coasts. When suddenly exposed it will very
likely stand its ground and defend itself with its
claws held up ready for action. This is no
empty threat, and it is wise to avoid handling
larger specimens with bare hands, as the nip is
quite powerful. The red eyes are unique
among our crabs, and enable instant
identification, although the structure of the
rear legs, noticeably flattened as paddles used
for swimming, is not found in any other
shore-living crabs.

CRUSTACEANS

J	F	M	A	M	J
J	A	S	O	N	D

Green Shore Crab
Carcinus maenas

ID FACT FILE

SIZE:
Carapace to
6 cm long

DESCRIPTION:
Carapace slightly
broader than
long, surface
with irregular
wrinkles, dark
green to
blackish, often
mottled paler,
very variable.
Three equal-sized
lobes between
eyes. Five teeth
on either side of
carapace

HABITAT:
Upper-shore
downwards on
every type of
coast

LOOKALIKES:
See other crabs

This is by far the commonest crab on all
European coasts, and unlike most of the
others, is not restricted to rocky shores, but is
found on mud and sand as well as in the
brackish conditions of saltmarshes and
estuaries. It occurs much further up the shore
than any other crab, occurring in rock pools on
the upper shore. Newly moulted specimens,
known as 'peelers', are often found sitting
beside their newly cast skins. Females 'in
berry' carrying a large mass of eggs (up to
185,000) are often quite noticeable in summer.
As in all crabs, the larvae become part of
the plankton.

CRUSTACEANS

J	F	M	A	M	J
J	A	S	O	N	D

Hairy Crab
Pilumnus hirtellus

ID FACT FILE

Size:
Carapace to
1.5 cm long

Description:
Carapace slightly
broader than
long, pale brown,
with five sharp
teeth on either
side of the eyes.
Carapace and all
walking legs
densely covered
in long hairs.
Pincers of
unequal size,
not hairy

Habitat:
Lower shore of
rocky coasts

Lookalikes:
See Broad-
clawed Porcelain
Crab, *Porcellana
platycheles*, page
139

In the Hairy Crab the body is much deeper
than in the other common hair-covered crab of
the lower shore, the Broad-clawed Porcelain
Crab, *Porcellana platycheles*, see page 139,
which has a very flat body. It also has densely
hairy pincers, which are of almost equal size,
unlike in the Hairy Crab in which one pincer is
about twice as big as the other and without
hairs, being smooth and shiny. The Hairy Crab
can be found beneath rocks around all suitable
coastlines in Britain and continental Europe as
far south as the Mediterranean.

CRUSTACEANS

J	F	M	A	M	J
J	A	S	O	N	D

Furrowed Crab

Xantho incisus

ID FACT FILE

SIZE:
Carapace up to
5 cm long and
8 cm broad

DESCRIPTION:
Carapace brown,
massively built
with a fairly
smooth surface
crossed by a
number of deep
furrows. Pincers
heavily built,
smooth and
glossy, with black
tips. Legs
without
noticeable hairs

HABITAT:
Under rocks on
lower shore

LOOKALIKES:
See Brown-
clawed Furrowed
Crab, *X. pilipes*,
page 150

This impressive crab has a very restricted
distribution in northern Europe, being found
on the shores of southwest England and the
west coast of Ireland, but not along the coasts
of continental Europe north of the
Mediterranean. Some books give the
maximum length of the carapace as about
2 cm, but specimens much larger than this are
common on some rocky shores on the south
coast of Cornwall. Although its distribution is
very scattered in southwest England, it can be
very abundant where it does occur.

CRUSTACEANS

Brown-clawed Furrowed Crab

Xantho pilipes

ID FACT FILE

SIZE:
Carapace to
about 3 cm long
and 5 cm broad

DESCRIPTION:
Carapace much
as in the
preceding
species, but
generally not so
distinctly
furrowed. Pincers
glossy with dark
brown tips.
Walking legs with
dense fringes of
long hairs

HABITAT:
Under rocks on
lower shore

LOOKALIKES:
See Furrowed
Crab, *X. incisus*,
page 149

This species has a much wider distribution
than the Furrowed Crab, in Britain being
found up the west coast as far north as
Shetland, and along the coast of mainland
Europe from Sweden to the Mediterranean.
That said, where the two species occur
together, as on the south coast of Cornwall, the
Furrowed Crab tends to be far more abundant.
In such cases there is no question about which
is which, as the long hairs fringing the legs of
X. pilipes are very conspicuous, especially in
water. The dark brown tips to the pincers
should also be a giveaway, but when wet they
tend to look almost as black as in *X. incisus*.

SPIDERS

J	F	M	A	M	J
J	A	S	O	N	D

ID FACT FILE

SIZE:
Body to 8 mm
long, legs to
1.5 cm

DESCRIPTION:
Body very thin
and flat, divided
into several
segments,
brownish-yellow.
Legs eight, very
long and slender

HABITAT:
Under rocks and
among seaweed
and hydroids on
lower shore

LOOKALIKES:
Several similar
species, either
smaller, much
fatter or only
distinguished on
microscopic
details

Common Sea-spider
Nymphon gracile

Sea-spiders are strange, gangling very distant relatives of terrestrial spiders. Due to their small size and spindly construction they are very difficult to spot on the seashore, where they are well camouflaged and may easily be missed. The head bears a bulbous proboscis used for piercing the bodies of prey such as sea anemones. On the underside of most species there is a pair of structures called ovigers used for holding eggs. The body is so slender that the digestive organs run up into the legs. This species is common on all coasts.

SPIDERS

J	F	M	A	M	J
J	A	S	O	N	D

Sand Wolf Spider
Arctosa perita

ID FACT FILE

SIZE:
Body 5–9 mm long

DESCRIPTION:
Body sand-coloured, blotched with black, brown and red, rather squat. Legs fairly long, eight in number, decorated with a series of light and dark rings

HABITAT:
On sand dunes, the tops of sandy shores and in similar places inland

SEASON:
Adults April–October

LOOKALIKES:
Small species of *Pardosa*, which tend to be much darker; see also Dune Wolf Spider, *Xerolycosa miniata*, opposite

This is one of several species of wolf spiders in the family Lycosidae that can be found around our coasts. Only two are common on sand dunes and beaches, this species and the next. *A. perita* generally spends much of its time in a burrow in the sand, from which it rushes out to pounce on passing insects. They will also emerge and quarter the sand nearby for prey. They are easy to spot when moving, but if they sense danger they 'freeze' and flatten themselves against the sand, becoming invisible. This species is widespread on sandy coasts and on sandy heaths inland.

Dune Wolf Spider

Xerolycosa miniata

J	F	M	A	M	J
J	A	S	O	N	D

ID FACT FILE

SIZE:
Body 4.5–7 mm
long

DESCRIPTION:
Colour generally
pale; abdomen
slightly darker on
top, marked with
a series of pale
chevrons. Sides
of cephalothorax
(the area behind
the head) dark.
Legs eight, only
partly decorated
with alternate
light and dark
bands

HABITAT:
Sand dunes

SEASON:
Adults
May–August

LOOKALIKES:
Pardosa wolf
spiders are much
darker and less
common on open
sand. See also
Sand Wolf
Spider, *Arctosa
perita*, opposite

Unlike the rather similar Sand Wolf Spider,
Arctosa perita, see opposite, this species
spends its entire life in the open running
around in search of insect prey on the surface
of the sand. Wolf spiders do not construct a
web in order to catch prey, but run it down in a
chase or make a capture from ambush. Silk is
used mainly as a covering for the spherical
white egg-sac, which in mid-summer can be
seen attached to the spinnerets beneath the tip
of the female's abdomen (see illustration). She
carries the eggs around until they hatch. This
species is widespread on all sandy coasts.

SPIDERS

Bordered Orb-weaver Spider

Neoscona adianta

ID FACT FILE

SIZE:
Female body
5–8 mm long;
male 4–5 mm

DESCRIPTION:
Abdomen plump,
rather rounded,
ground colour
variable, from
gingery brown to
rich brownish-
red, with series
of angular white
marks down
either side of the
midline

HABITAT:
Coastal
grasslands and
scrubby areas

SEASON:
Adult July–August

LOOKALIKES:
Garden Spider,
*Araneus
diadematus* is
bigger, plain
brown with white
'cross' on
abdomen; Gorse
Orb-weaver,
Agalenatea redii
has circular, dark
brown abdomen

This is one of the most attractive of the
orb-weavers that occur in northern Europe. It
is seldom found more than 200 m from the sea,
typically living among long grass, gorse and
other scrub on cliff tops. The female (which is
the sex most often seen) spends most of her
time sitting on nearby plants rather than in her
web, and can be surprisingly difficult to spot
because her pattern is designed to break up
her outline. Unlike in some orb-web spiders,
the females are generally very cooperative with
the rather smaller males. It is absent from
Scotland and northernmost England, but
widespread in mainland Europe.

INSECTS

J	F	M	A	M	J
J	A	S	O	N	D

Shore Bristletail
Petrobius maritimus

ID FACT FILE

SIZE:
Body to 1.5 cm long

DESCRIPTION:
Body shaped like a shuttle, tapering towards the rear end. Eyes large and prominent. Antennae as long as or longer than body, bristly. One long central 'tail' flanked by a shorter one on each side. Six legs

HABITAT:
Upper shore

SEASON:
All year

LOOKALIKES:
None on shore

The body of this small animal is clothed with scales, giving it a glossy appearance as it moves around. It can be very common on damp cliff faces at the top of the shore, where sometimes hundreds of individuals of all ages may be swarming over rocks at low tide, scavenging on whatever edible material they can find. Juveniles just resemble smaller versions of the adults. It belongs to the insect order Thysanura, and is common on coasts throughout northern Europe.

INSECTS

Short-winged Cone-head
Conocephalus dorsalis

J	F	M	A	M	J
J	A	S	O	N	D

ID FACT FILE

SIZE:
11–17 mm

DESCRIPTION:
Body green, fairly long and narrow, more or less slab-sided. Antennae very long and hair-like. Last pair of legs long and powerful, built for jumping. Wings normally absent. Face with receding 'chin'

HABITAT:
Saltmarshes and in long grass in damp places near the sea

SEASON:
Adult August–September

LOOKALIKES:
The Long-winged Cone-head, *C. discolor* is always fully winged. Female has straight ovipositor. It prefers drier areas, such as cliff faces, but is also found in damp areas near the coast

Although basically green, this small bush-cricket has a brown stripe down the centre of the back. In females there is a long and very prominent upcurved ovipositor resembling a small sabre jutting out from the rear end (see illustration). This is used to cut a slit into the stems of sedges, rushes and other plants in order to insert the eggs. A single female can lay as many as 100 eggs. The nymphs are also green and resemble miniature adults. This species is often present in huge numbers in suitable localities, mainly in the south of Britain, not in Ireland, but over a wide area in continental Europe. Fully winged specimens are sometimes present.

INSECTS

J	F	M	A	M	J
J	A	S	O	N	D

Roesel's Bush-cricket
Metrioptera roeselii

ID FACT FILE

SIZE:
13–17 mm

DESCRIPTION:
Body quite
stoutly built,
brown or green
with yellow
markings on
the side of the
thorax. Hind
legs long and
powerful, built for
jumping.
Antennae long
and whip-like.
Forewings
reduced to
short flaps

HABITAT:
Mainly in lush
grassland near
estuaries, also
more rarely
inland

SEASON:
Adult July–
October

LOOKALIKES:
The Dark
Bush-cricket,
*Pholidoptera
griseoaptera* has
no yellow marks
on the sides and
no wing-flaps;
The Grey
Bush-Cricket,
*Platycleis
denticulata* is
fully winged and
prefers dry,
sunny cliff faces

As in the Short-winged Cone-head,
Conocephalus dorsalis, see opposite, fully
winged individuals of this much larger
bush-cricket are sometimes present among
thousands of wingless specimens. Females
have an upturned, sabre-like ovipositor used
for laying eggs in grass stems. Nymphs are
generally seen from about May onwards, and
the first adults are found from late July, usually
dying off by the end of October. Its rather
inconspicuous 'song' is given during the day.
The main item of food is probably grass. In
Britain this is mainly an insect of the east coast,
up to Yorkshire, but it is far more widespread
on the European mainland.

J	F	M	A	M	J
J	A	S	O	N	D

INSECTS

Great Green Bush-cricket

Tettigonia viridissima

ID FACT FILE

SIZE:
40–54 mm

DESCRIPTION:
Body large, stout, green, with very well-developed wings and very long, whip-like antennae. Hind legs long, well-developed. Ovipositor in female very long (about 2 cm) and tapering, almost straight

HABITAT:
Open, well-vegetated places near the sea; much less common inland

SEASON:
Adult July–September

LOOKALIKES:
The Wart-biter, *Decticus verrucivorus* is shorter and stouter, speckled with black, and in the female the ovipositor is strongly upcurved

This is the largest bush-cricket and one of the largest insects in Europe. The harsh, high-pitched song of the males is given from a concealed perch in long bursts, carrying for a considerable distance and clearly audible from a passing car. Trying to track down the singer can be a long and frustrating waste of time. This impressive insect is most likely to be found as it jumps away in front of you as you walk through long vegetation near the sea, mainly in the south of Britain (not in Ireland). It is much more widespread in continental Europe.

INSECTS

Dune Spurge Bug
Dicranocephalus agilis

ID FACT FILE

SIZE:
12–14 mm

DESCRIPTION:
Body rather elongated, black, head rather pointed. Antennae just over half as long as body, with alternate broad black and white rings. Legs similarly marked. Row of pale spots around rear margin of abdomen

HABITAT:
Sand dunes

SEASON:
Adult June–August

LOOKALIKES:
None

This rather dark but very distinctive bug is most likely to be seen perched feeding on the flowers of Portland Spurge, *Euphorbia portlandica*, see page 81, and to a lesser extent Sea Spurge, *E. paralias*, see page 82, on coastal sand dunes. In the British Isles it is rather local, being scattered around the coast from Kent to west Wales, as well as in southern Ireland, but it is more widespread on the coasts of mainland Europe. The bugs overwinter as adults, and can be found mating on spurge flowers in May and June.

Dune Bee Fly
Villa modesta

ID FACT FILE

SIZE:
10–13 mm

DESCRIPTION:
Body elongate-
oval, quite
densely covered
with brownish-red
hairs. A single
pair of wings
which are
transparent and
without dark
markings except
for a narrow
brown front
margin.
Proboscis short

HABITAT:
Coastal sand
dunes; in
mainland Europe
also in sandy
places inland

SEASON:
May–July

LOOKALIKES:
None in Britain;
several other
similar difficult-
to-separate
species in
mainland Europe

This distinctive fly occurs on most of the larger
(and many smaller) dune systems up the coasts
of England and Wales, and up the east coast of
Scotland, as well as southeast Ireland. It is
more widespread in mainland Europe,
occurring inland as well as on the coast. It is
most likely to be seen basking on the sand in
the hollow of a coastal dune. The insect illustrated is a female which was picking up sand
grains in a special pocket at the tip of her
abdomen. These are used to coat her eggs.
The larvae are parasites of caterpillars.

INSECTS

Fan-bristled Robber Fly

Dysmachus trigonus

|J|F|M|A|M|J|
|J|A|S|O|N|D|

ID FACT FILE

SIZE:
10–16 mm

DESCRIPTION:
Body dark, with a rather hunch-backed look due to the very bulging, convex top of the thorax, which is hairy and bristly. Abdomen tapering, dark brownish-grey. Wings two, transparent, with brown bases

HABITAT:
On coastal sand dunes; more rarely on sandy heaths inland

SEASON:
Late May–early July

LOOKALIKES:
The Dune Robber Fly, *Philonicus albiceps* is up to 18 mm, abdomen paler, ash-grey, thorax not so humped, not bristly; Pied-winged Robber Fly, *Pamponerus germanicus*, body dark, to 19 mm long, with patterned wings

Robber flies are predators that capture other insects on the wing. This species catches a variety of other insects such as beetles and wasps, but prefers flies. In some areas it seems particularly fond of capturing the Coastal Silver-Stiletto Fly, *Thereva annulata*, see page 162. Feeding usually takes place on the surface of the sand and takes some time as the prey's juices are sucked out. Cannibalism is quite common and other large robber flies may fall victim. This species is widespread around the coasts of Britain, although much commoner in the south and of wide distribution in continental Europe.

INSECTS

Coastal Silver-stiletto Fly
Thereva annulata

ID FACT FILE

SIZE:
8–11 mm

DESCRIPTION:
Male (illustrated) with slim, slightly tapering abdomen, covered in a dense pile of silvery hairs. Top of thorax silvery-grey. Female abdomen more tapering, dull greyish-brown. Wings two, clear

HABITAT:
Coastal sand dunes

SEASON:
May–September

LOOKALIKES:
Swollen Silver-stiletto Fly, *Dialineura anilis* smaller, male less silvery, with brown top to thorax; female dull brown

In more recent books this is included in the genus *Acrosathe*, but will undoubtedly one day return to *Thereva*, where it belongs. The silvery males are most attractive and are often seen basking rather inconspicuously on patches of bare sand. Mating pairs sit facing in opposite directions, joined at the tip of the abdomen. The females are less often seen, but can sometimes be found half-buried in the sand as they push down into it with their abdomen, laying their eggs. This fly is widespread on dune systems throughout much of Europe.

INSECTS

Common Sand Wasp
Ammophila sabulosa

J	F	M	A	M	J
J	A	S	O	N	D

ID FACT FILE

SIZE:
15–25 mm

DESCRIPTION:
Body long and slender, with a thread-like 'waist', oranged-red towards rear end, with a black tip. Wings four, rather smoky. Legs long and slender. Antennae dark

HABITAT:
Mostly on sand dunes, also sandy cliffs; rarer inland on heaths

SEASON:
June–September

LOOKALIKES:
Various species of *Podalonia* have shorter, thicker bodies

This species varies greatly in size, and the males are always smaller than the females. When in flight the abdomen is held upwards at an angle relative to the head and thorax. Females are mostly seen quartering the sand rapidly in search of their prey, the smooth-bodied caterpillars of various moths. More rarely a female will be seen trundling back to her nest with a paralysed caterpillar slung beneath her body. This will provide sufficient living food for a single wasp larva. In Britain distribution is mainly in the south; in Europe this wasp is widespread.

INSECTS

J	F	M	A	M	J
J	A	S	O	N	D

Leaden Spider Wasp
Pompilus cinereus

ID FACT FILE

SIZE:
8–10 mm

DESCRIPTION:
Body slender, greyish-black, wings dark. Legs relatively long, built for running across sand

HABITAT:
Coastal dunes and sandy places inland

SEASON:
May–August

LOOKALIKES:
Several similar species in various genera, some with red on abdomen, all difficult to tell apart

This is one of several small, slim and very active wasps that run around on the bare sand in search of spiders. After being stung and paralysed, these are towed back to a suitable spot for nesting, usually in bare sand that is not too loose. The wasp then buries the spider temporarily in order to hide it from ants and other possible thieves while she is busy elsewhere digging her nest. The spider is finally entombed at the bottom of the nest where it provides fresh food for a single larva. It is widespread both in Europe and most of the British Isles.

INSECTS

Dune Snail Bee
Osmia aurulenta

J	F	M	A	M	J
J	A	S	O	N	D

ID FACT FILE

Size:
8–11 mm

Description:
Body in both sexes quite densely covered with short hairs which are gingery-brown in females but silvery-black and far less dense in males. Pollen-collecting hairs forming a brush on underside of abdomen

Habitat:
Coastal sand dunes, much rarer on heaths inland

Season:
May–June

Lookalikes:
There are many other similar-looking bees, difficult to tell apart but mostly not nesting in snail shells (never so on British coasts)

This bee has fascinating nesting habits, which in the British Isles are shared with only one other (solely inland) species. The female seeks out empty snail shells, which are usually abundant on coastal dunes. Inside the larger shells she builds several cells divided by internal partitions. She stocks each cell with a mixture of pollen and nectar gathered from flowers. She then seals up the opening in the shell with a curtain made of chewed-up leaves. This interesting behaviour can be seen around the south and west coasts of Britain, on the east coast of Ireland and quite widely in Europe.

INSECTS

J	F	M	A	M	J
J	A	S	O	N	D

Silvery Leafcutter Bee
Megachile dorsalis

ID FACT FILE

Size:
8–11 mm

Description:
Female black, with lines of short silvery hairs along margins of abdominal segments and silvery brush of pollen-collecting hairs on underside of abdomen. Male brown

Habitat:
Sand dunes, even when only very tiny at the tops of beaches

Season:
May–August

Lookalikes:
Several similar species, mostly larger. See also previous page

This is the smallest of several leafcutter bees found on dunes, the largest being *M. maritima*, which is brown. All species share similar habits, snipping semicircular sections out of leaves (usually willow in this species) and ferrying them back to their nests in the sand. These form dense, bustling colonies, with bees coming and going all the time. The leaf sections are used to form a stubby cigar-shaped cell within the nest. This is stocked with pollen and nectar. In Britain this bee is locally scattered around the south coast, but is widespread in Europe.

INSECTS

Hairy-legged Mining Bee
Dasypoda altercator

J	F	M	A	M	J
J	A	S	O	N	D

ID FACT FILE

Size:
13–15 mm

Description:
Rather like a much hairier version of the familiar Honey Bee, *Apis mellifera*. Back legs very distinctive being clothed in a dense brush of long, silky hairs

Habitat:
Sandy bare places on the coast and inland

Season:
July–August

Lookalikes:
Many other solitary bees, but not having such hairy back legs

When walking down to the beach along a sandy path you may have to be careful not to tread on a female of this charming little bee returning to her nest in the hard-packed bare ground of the path, which is preferred over the softer sand of the dunes. She will probably be covered in a thick coat of yellow pollen which is collected all over her hairy body. Large clumps of pollen are also carried on the thick brush of hairs on the hind legs. Nests often occur in large colonies. In the British Isles this bee has declined greatly and it is now classed as Nationally Scarce, occurring only around the south coast from Norfolk to north Wales. It is more widespread in Europe.

INSECTS

Dune Chafer
Anomala dubia

J	F	M	A	M	J
J	A	S	O	N	D

ID FACT FILE

SIZE:
12–15 mm

DESCRIPTION:
Body rotund, domed on top, flatter beneath. Head and thorax dark metallic green, covered in fine dot-like punctures. Thorax with wavy brown lower margin. Wing cases brown with a greenish tinge. Antennae short, elbowed. Legs spiny

HABITAT:
Sand dunes

SEASON:
June–August

LOOKALIKES:
The Garden Chafer, *Phyllopertha horticola* is smaller (8–12 mm) and has an all-green thorax

Large swarms of this attractive little chafer suddenly hatch from pupae buried in the sand, the plump larvae having fed on the roots of various plants. For a few days the males are everywhere, furiously chasing the females and often forming a struggling scrummage as they fight for the right to mate. Such frenetic activity only takes place in warm sunshine, and if a cloud covers the sun, the beetles all disappear, often sitting inside flowers whose petals they eat. Distribution in Britain is along the southern coasts, but is more widespread on the Continent.

INSECTS

Sulphur Dune Beetle
Cteniopus sulphureus

J	F	M	A	M	J
J	A	S	O	N	D

ID FACT FILE

SIZE:
4–5 mm

DESCRIPTION:
Legs and body bright sulphur yellow. Antennae slender, about half as long as head and body combined

HABITAT:
On sand dunes, more rarely in sandy places inland, such as heaths

SEASON:
May–August

LOOKALIKES:
None

In some books this beetle is included in the subfamily Alleculinae within the very large family of darkling beetles, the Tenebrionidae. In others, the subfamily is raised to full family status as the Alleculidae. The adults spend most of their time feeding on pollen and often gather in some numbers on the heads of favoured flowers, such as Wild Carrot, *Daucus carota*, see page 67, which may have 20 or more beetles contrasting with its white flowers. The larvae live in the sand near the base of various plants. This species is widespread on all coasts.

MOLLUSCS

| J | F | M | A | M | J |
| J | A | S | O | N | D |

Common Chiton
Lepidochitona cinerea

ID FACT FILE

SIZE:
To 2.5 cm

DESCRIPTION:
Forming an elongated oval hummock, colour variable, most often greenish-grey, also red, pinkish, brown or pale blue. Narrow girdle around lower margin, covered with small rounded granules and short, thick spines

HABITAT:
On rocks on lower shore

LOOKALIKES:
There are several other fairly common species on the shore, all difficult to tell apart. See also Keeled Chiton, *Acanthochitona, crinitus*, opposite

Chitons are also known as Coat-of-Mail shells on account of their body structure, consisting of eight arched plates which interlock flexibly along their margins, like the chain mail used by the knights of old. Chitons spend their lives clamped down against rocks by their broad, muscular foot. They graze on algae, moving very slowly forwards across the wet surface. This is the commonest European species, being found on all coasts.

MOLLUSCS

Keeled Chiton

Acanthochitona crinitus

ID FACT FILE

SIZE:
To 3 cm

DESCRIPTION:
Body slightly
elongated oval,
greenish-grey,
often with black
tinges. Shell
plates have
raised keels.
Girdle with 18
tufts of quite
long bristles at
regularly spaced
intervals

HABITAT:
On rocks on
lower shore

LOOKALIKES:
Other chitons,
all rather similar.
See also
Common Chiton,
*Lepidochitona
cinerea*, opposite

This is the spiniest of the common chitons
found between tidemarks and is widespread all
round the coasts of Europe. You will need a
lens in order to distinguish the keels on the
plates and the presence of the tufts of long
spines around the girdle. However, even with
the naked eye this species looks spinier than
the Common Chiton, *Lepidochitona cinerea*,
see opposite. Chitons breathe via gills situated
in a series of pairs in slits on either side of the
body. Although most often found by turning
over stones, chitons can also be spotted on the
sides of rock pools.

J	F	M	A	M	J
J	A	S	O	N	D

Common Limpet
Patella vulgata

ID FACT FILE

SIZE:
To 6 cm long

DESCRIPTION:
Shell conical, thick and heavy, marked with a series of coarse ridges radiating outwards from the apex. Colour variable, often greyish on wave-beaten exposed coasts, otherwise whitish marked with brown, often with blue tinges. Sole of foot yellowish, dull orange or brown

HABITAT:
On rocks at all levels of the shore

LOOKALIKES:
Black Footed Limpet, *P. depressa* is smaller (to 3 cm), flatter and has black sole. China Limpet, *P. ulyssiponensis* has apricot foot

This ubiquitous species is the only limpet you are likely to encounter on most shores, where it often covers the rocks in countless numbers. With their low, streamlined shape and powerfully clinging foot, limpets are well able to resist being dislodged by the pounding of the waves. Each one has its own favourite spot to which it will return, following a mucous trail, after making a feeding foray at high tide, grazing on algae on the rock surface. When chemicals used to treat oil spills wipe out the limpets temporarily, the rocks soon become covered in algae.

MOLLUSCS

Blue-rayed Limpet

Helcion pellucidum

ID FACT FILE

Size:
To 1.5 cm

Description:
Shell oval, shaped like a cap and with the slightly pointed apex offset towards one end, shiny translucent brown, with several rows of brilliant bright blue spots

Habitat:
Lower shore, on kelps

Lookalikes:
None

Because of its small size this lovely species takes some searching for. The fact that it usually lives in small groups is a help, but you will still have to turn over the wet blades and stems of kelps such as Oarweed, *Laminaria digitata*, see page 14. in order to find it, because this is the only place it lives. Kelp provides its sole food and each limpet grazes out a deep groove, which may weaken the stems so much that they are torn free during stormy weather. Although widespread on European coasts, the Blue-rayed Limpet is absent from Holland, Belgium, Denmark and the Baltic.

Toothed or Thick Top Shell

Monodonta lineata

J	F	M	A	M	J
J	A	S	O	N	D

ID FACT FILE

SIZE:
Shell to 3 cm high

DESCRIPTION:
Shell a rather tall, thick, heavily built cone of just five or six whorls giving a rather plump, rounded appearance. Colour light brown, with a zigzag pattern of green and reddish-brown markings

HABITAT:
Middle and upper shore, on rocks

LOOKALIKES:
Common Periwinkle, *Littorina littorea*, page 179, has a taller, less round-profiled, plain brownish or blackish shell. See also other top shells

This relatively large top shell can be extremely abundant on some shores, often occurring as dense masses along the edges of rock pools. It can withstand long periods of exposure sitting high and dry in the heat of the sun during low tides. It can also withstand considerable exposure to wave action, although on wave-pounded shores the shells become very rounded and worn, with most of the colour removed. This is a southern species in Britain and Ireland, present only on Atlantic and Channel coasts in Europe.

MOLLUSCS

Grey Top Shell
Gibbula cinerea

J	F	M	A	M	J
J	A	S	O	N	D

ID FACT FILE

SIZE:
Shell to 1.5 cm
high

DESCRIPTION:
Shell rather
rounded in
outline, coming
to a slightly
pointed,
nipple-like apex.
Colour grey, with
a pattern of
narrow,
zigzagging bands
of brownish-red

HABITAT:
From middle
shore downwards

LOOKALIKES:
See other
top shells

Easily distinguished from other top shells by size, shape and the patterning on its shell, this species is also distinguished by its habit of living out of sight beneath rocks or seaweeds, or in rock crevices. These will therefore have to be moved aside in order to reveal this species, which usually occurs in small groups. All the other top shells live in full view on top of rocks. Top shells graze on rocky surfaces, feeding on minute algae and other detritus. This species is found along rocky coasts throughout northern Europe.

MOLLUSCS

Flat Top Shell

Gibbula umbilicalis

| J | F | M | A | M | J |
| J | A | S | O | N | D |

ID FACT FILE

SIZE:
Shell to 13 mm high

DESCRIPTION:
Shell slightly flatter than in the preceding species, with a marginally blunter apex. Ground colour dull greenish, marked with fairly broad and straight bands of reddish-brown or reddish-purple

HABITAT:
From upper shore rock pools to lower shore on rocks

LOOKALIKES:
See other top shells

This attractive species is often abundant in rock pools on the upper and middle shore and just about anywhere on the lower shore. The greenish ground colour and broader, non-zigzagged bands easily distinguish it from the Grey Top shell. *G. cinerea*, see page 175, with which it may occur on the middle shore. The Flat Top shell breeds during summer and its larvae settle on rocks after only a few days as members of the plankton. Although common along the western coast of Britain, around all of Ireland and along the Atlantic coasts of Europe, this species is absent from North Sea coasts.

MOLLUSCS

| J | F | M | A | M | J |
| J | A | S | O | N | D |

Painted Top Shell
Calliostoma zizyphinum

ID FACT FILE

SIZE:
Shell about 3 cm high and wide across the base

DESCRIPTION:
Shell perfectly conical, coming almost to a point at the top, with about 10 strongly ribbed whorls and a squarish aperture. Colour brownish-orange with variable amounts of white specking visible; occasionally all-white

HABITAT:
Lower shore, on rock

LOOKALIKES:
Shell larger and more perfectly conical than other species of common top shells on the shore. *C. laugieri* (Mediterranean only) smaller, more marbled, with narrower, more pointed shell. Most similar is Turban Top shell, *Gibbula magus*, see page 178. *G. divaricata* (south Portugal east to Mediterranean) paler and more bluntly conical

With its bright colour and perfectly straight-sided conical shape the Painted Top shell is easily recognised. It is absent from the upper and middle shore where some of the commoner top shells abound, but prefers rocky areas nearer to the low-water mark where it is only exposed by relatively low tides. It is usually found clinging singly to the undersides of rock overhangs, but may also sometimes occur in small groups. White-shelled specimens also occur. The eggs are laid in long jelly-like strings and give rise to miniatures of the adults. A widespread species.

MOLLUSCS

J	F	M	A	M	J
J	A	S	O	N	D

Turban Top Shell
Gibbula magus

ID FACT FILE

SIZE:
To 3 cm high

DESCRIPTION:
Viewed in profile
whorls rise in
noticeably
stepped fashion,
eight in all. Basic
colour yellowish,
dull grey or
white, overlain by
splashes of
brown, red or
purple

HABITAT:
Lower shore

LOOKALIKES:
See other
top shells

Although empty shells of this distinctive
mollusc are sometimes found higher up the
shore, in order to see one alive you will have to
search the lowermost part of the shore exposed
only during the lowest spring tides of the year.
Even then, only the odd solitary individual is
likely to show up. The Turban Top shell is also
less fond of clean rock than the others,
preferring rocky shores overlain by sand
and muddy gravel. It is found all round the
coasts of Ireland, up the west coast of Britain
(except in south Wales), but not on the east
coast; from the Gulf of St Malo southwards to
the Mediterranean.

Common or Edible Periwinkle

Littorina littorea

J	F	M	A	M	J
J	A	S	O	N	D

ID FACT FILE

SIZE:
Shell to 3 cm
high

DESCRIPTION:
Shell black or
dark brown, paler
when dry, rather
plump and
globular at base
but tapering
upwards to a
distinct spire,
each whorl with a
surface sculpture
of fine grooves

HABITAT:
Between
tidemarks on
rocky shores,
often most
abundant on
middle shore

LOOKALIKES:
See Toothed
Top Shell,
*Monodonta
lineata*,
page 174

This species often occurs in vast numbers lying around in dense aggregations on sheltered, weedy and rocky shores. The aperture of the shell can be completely closed with a hard, horny flap-like operculum. The jelly-like egg capsules are shed directly into the sea. Like all periwinkles this is a grazer, feeding on algae growing on rock surfaces. This species is considered a delicacy by some people, and it is heavily collected in many areas, being cooked first before being eaten. It is still widespread around the coasts of northern Europe.

MOLLUSCS

J	F	M	A	M	J
J	A	S	O	N	D

Flat Periwinkle
Littorina obtusata

ID FACT FILE

SIZE:
Shell to 1.5 cm high

DESCRIPTION:
Shell broad and flat-topped, with only the slight suggestion of a spire. Colour variable, black, dark brown, various shades of green, yellow, orange, dark red or purple

HABITAT:
On wracks on middle shore

LOOKALIKES:
L. mariae is almost identical but lives only on Toothed Wrack

With its distinctly flattened shell this is quite different from any other periwinkles. Its colour easily distinguishes it from the Flat Top shell, *Gibbula umbilicalis*, see page 176, which does not live on seaweeds. The Flat Periwinkle lives and feeds on large brown seaweeds, almost exclusively Knotted Wrack, *Ascophyllum nodosum*, see page 19, and Bladder Wrack, *Fucus vesiculosus*, see page 22. Individuals having brownish-green shells greatly resemble the bladders of the latter species. The jelly-like egg masses are deposited on the seaweeds and hatch as crawling (i.e. non-planktonic) youngsters. Found on all coasts.

MOLLUSCS

J	F	M	A	M	J
J	A	S	O	N	D

Small Periwinkle
Littorina neritoides

ID FACT FILE

SIZE:
Shell under
1 cm high

DESCRIPTION:
Shell grey, rather
narrow in profile
with a high,
pointed spire,
surface of
body-whorl with
clearly marked
growth bands.
Aperture oval

HABITAT:
At the very top of
rocky shores

LOOKALIKES:
See Rough
Periwinkle,
L. saxatilis,
page 182

This is by far the tiniest of our periwinkles, and
it occurs higher up the shore than any others.
It can usually be found in rock crevices right at
the top of the shore. It reaches high up on the
cliffs well above the high-water mark, right to
the limit of where salt spray from stormy seas
can reach, although it may remain unwetted
for days or even weeks on end. It feeds by
grazing on the abundant lichens in its habitat.
Egg capsules are released in winter during
storms which can drench even the highest
cliffs in spray. Found on all coasts except the
Channel and southern North Sea.

MOLLUSCS

| J | F | M | A | M | J |
| J | A | S | O | N | D |

Rough Periwinkle
Littorina saxatilis

ID FACT FILE

SIZE:
Shell to 18 mm high

DESCRIPTION:
Shell fairly broad, with well-defined spire and covered with numerous spiral grooves which give the shell a rough feel when handled. Colour variable – red, orange and black most common

HABITAT:
Mainly rocks of upper shore, also on mud in estuaries

LOOKALIKES:
See Small Periwinkle, *L. neritoides*, page 181

This very variably coloured species is found just below the very high, exposed zone inhabited by the Small Periwinkle, *L. neritoides*, see page 181, being common on rocks, cliff faces and among large seaweeds at the top of the shore where high tides normally reach. Groups of individuals of different colours are usually found together. Eggs develop fully within the female and are released as active juveniles, which resemble miniature adults and are able to establish themselves immediately on the shore. This common species is found on all coasts.

MOLLUSCS

Chinaman's Hat
Calyptraea chinensis

J	F	M	A	M	J
J	A	S	O	N	D

ID FACT FILE

SIZE:
Shell to 15 mm across, 5 mm high

DESCRIPTION:
Shell forming an almost perfectly symmetrical brownish or whitish cone which scarcely rises above the rock to which it is fixed

HABITAT:
On stones on muddy shores at extreme low-water mark

LOOKALIKES:
None

Also called the Cup-and-Saucer Limpet, this species is rather local, being found on the north and west coasts of Britain and Ireland, but absent from all Channel and North Sea coasts. In very sheltered south coast bays in places such as Cornwall it can often be found spawning, but is only visible for a brief period during exceptionally low spring tides. Food particles are filtered out of the water and then bound together with mucous.

MOLLUSCS

American Slipper Limpet
Crepidula fornicata

J	F	M	A	M	J
J	A	S	O	N	D

ID FACT FILE

SIZE:
Shell to 5 cm long, 2.5 cm high

DESCRIPTION:
Shell pale brown, forming a long, oval mound with a small spire consisting of just two whorls at one end, usually pointing slightly downwards

HABITAT:
Attached to rocks in mud on the lower shore

LOOKALIKES:
None

This species was unintentionally introduced into Europe with oysters from North America in 1887 and is now widely established around most of Europe's coastlines, where in some places it has unfortunately replaced the native oyster. Several specimens are usually found heaped one atop the other, forming chains of from two to ten or more individuals. The largest (lowermost) member of the chain will be female, the outermost, smallest will be male and those in between will be in the process of switching from male to female.

MOLLUSCS

Spotted Cowrie
Trivia monacha

J	F	M	A	M	J
J	A	S	O	N	D

ID FACT FILE

SIZE:
Shell to 12 mm long

DESCRIPTION:
Shell egg-shaped, flattened on the lowermost side where the aperture is situated, with a series of thick ridges running across the shell at right angles to the aperture. Colour brownish-white, with three darker brown spots

HABITAT:
On and under rocks on lower shore

LOOKALIKES:
The Arctic Cowrie, *T. arctica* is smaller (to 1 cm), whiter and has no dark spots (see right, lower two shells)

Cowries are mainly tropical and there are only five species in European waters. The shape of the shell is diagnostic and cannot be mistaken for anything else. Cowries are usually found clinging to the sheltered undersides of overhanging rocks at low tide, or beneath stones, but are only exposed during the lowest spring tides of the year. They are usually in close proximity to their main food, the Star Ascidians *Botryllus schlosseri* and *Botrylloides leachi*, see page 230. The Spotted Cowrie (see top shell below) is widespread on western coasts, but is absent from the North Sea and Scandinavia.

MOLLUSCS

Necklace Shell
Polinices catenus

ID FACT FILE

SIZE:
Shell to 3 cm
high

DESCRIPTION:
Shell more or
less globular,
with a rather
stepped, conical
spire, very pale
brown and
unpatterned
except for a
single darker
band on the
body whorl

HABITAT:
In sand on lower
shore

LOOKALIKES:
See Alder's Neck-
lace Shell, *P.
polianus*,
opposite

As with many sand-dwelling molluscs, you are
more likely to come across empty shells on the
surface of the sand rather than the living
animal. However, during very low tides active
individuals that are very much alive may be
visible protruding onto the surface of the sand
or even on it. The foot is thick and broad and is
folded upwards around the sides of the shell as
the animal crawls, being able to cover most of
the shell as a defensive measure. Necklace
Shells are carnivores, and this widely spread
species mainly feeds on tellins.

J	F	M	A	M	J
J	A	S	O	N	D

Alder's Necklace Shell

Polinices polianus

ID FACT FILE

SIZE:
Shell to 16 mm high

DESCRIPTION:
Shell less globular than in preceding species, with a low spire of up to seven whorls. Colour pale cream, with a bold pattern consisting of five spiral rows of dark brown markings on the body whorl

HABITAT:
In sand on lower shore

LOOKALIKES:
See Necklace Shell, *P. catenus*, see opposite

Apart from being much smaller than the Necklace Shell, *P. catenus,* see opposite, the boldly marked shell of this species is an easily seen diagnostic character. In necklace shells the sexes are separate and fertilisation takes place internally. The spawn consists of thick ribbons bound together with a mucous secretion mixed with grains of sand. Prey, consisting of bivalve molluscs, is hunted within the sand. Alder's Necklace Shell gains access to the closed shell of its prey by drilling a characteristic round hole in it. This species is common from west Norway to the Mediterranean.

MOLLUSCS

Dog Whelk
Nucella lapillus

ID FACT FILE

SIZE:
Shell to 4 cm or more high

DESCRIPTION:
Shell very thick and strong, broadly conical, tapering suddenly into a short spire. Colour white to yellow to grey to dark brown, plain or banded. Aperture oval

HABITAT:
Middle to lower shore, usually in rock crevices

LOOKALIKES:
See European Sting Winkle, *Ocenebra erinacea*, opposite, and also Netted Dog Whelk, *Hinia reticulata*, page 191, and Thick-lipped Dog Whelk, *H. incrassata*, page 192

Dog Whelks, found on all coasts, are often abundant near their prey which consists primarily of barnacles and mussels. As can be seen in the accompanying illustration, the shell of the Dog Whelk is very variable in colour, and individuals that have been feeding on dark-shelled mussels will themselves have darker shells. In summer the adults will often be found alongside their distinctive masses of flask-shaped yellow egg-capsules. From these juveniles hatch which remain on the shore and crawl rather than becoming free-swimming members of the plankton.

European Sting Winkle
Ocenebra erinacea

ID FACT FILE

SIZE:
Shell to 5 cm
long

DESCRIPTION:
Shell brownish-
white, tall and
slender, with a
prominent spire,
covered in broad
angular ribs and
broad striations
in a spiral
pattern, with a
rather irregularly
stepped and
usually untidy
profile

HABITAT:
On rocks on
lower shore

LOOKALIKES:
Juveniles can
resemble adults
of Thick-lipped
Dog Whelk, *Hinia
incrassata*, see
page 192. See
also Dog Whelk,
Nucella lapillus,
see opposite

The very angular and irregular profile of the
shell is the most distinctive feature of this
species, which you are only likely to find if you
visit the shore during a spring tide. It is a
predator of other molluscs such as cockles,
gaining access to the soft body by alternately
softening its victim's shell with an acid
secretion from the foot and then rasping away
the softened material with the radula
(mouthparts). Eggs are laid in large egg
capsules. Distribution is mainly southern and
western, excluding Scandinavia but including
the southern North Sea.

MOLLUSCS

J	F	M	A	M	J
J	A	S	O	N	D

Common Whelk
Buccinum undatum

ID FACT FILE

SIZE:
Shell to 11 cm long

DESCRIPTION:
Shell pale whitish-brown to dark brown or greenish, with a pointed spire of eight rounded whorls covered in numerous ridges and grooves giving an effect of overlapping tiles. Body of animal reddish-white with black flecks

HABITAT:
On rock, sand and gravel at extreme low water of spring tides

LOOKELIKES:
Only in deep water

On its size alone the Common Whelk, which is found on all our coasts, is a very impressive animal, although it is not really an inhabitant of the shore. However, during the exceptionally low tides that occur in March and April of some years, when the water drops well below its normal lowest point (chart datum) numbers of Common Whelks may be exposed for an hour or so. It feeds on other molluscs such as cockles, as well as worms and carrion. Its spongy whitish egg-masses are known as sea wash balls and are sometimes washed up on the strandline.

MOLLUSCS

J	F	M	A	M	J
J	A	S	O	N	D

Netted Dog Whelk

Hinia reticulata

ID FACT FILE

SIZE:
Shell to 3 cm
long

DESCRIPTION:
Shell rather
plump, brownish,
spire pointed,
consisting of up
to ten whorls, all
covered in a
net-like sculpture
of fairly deep ribs
intersected by a
series of closely
spaced spiral
grooves.
Aperture rather
narrowly
elongate-oval

HABITAT:
On muddy sand
and gravel
between rocks
on lower shore

LOOKALIKES:
See Dog Whelk,
Nucella lapillus,
page 188 and
Thick-lipped
Dog Whelk,
H. incrassata,
page 192

The fine net-like pattern and more pointed
shell in which the lower whorls grade more
evenly into the spire, should be sufficient to
distinguish this species from the Dog Whelk,
Nucella lapillus, see page 188, which also has a
different habitat (in rock crevices). Netted Dog
Whelks are more likely to be found crawling
over stones and gravel in pools on the lower
shore, around all coasts. They feed on carrion
rather than living animals, and lay their eggs in
flat, flask-shaped capsules attached in rows to
sea grasses, seaweeds and stones.

MOLLUSCS

Thick-lipped Dog Whelk
Hinia incrassata

ID FACT FILE

Size:
Shell to 12 mm long

Description:
Shell brownish, patterned with ribs and spiral grooves, and with a far more roundly oval aperture than in the preceding species

Habitat:
Lower shore, underneath stones and on fine muddy gravel

Lookalikes:
See Dog Whelk, *Nucella lapillus*, page 188, and Netted Dog Whelk, *H. reticulata*, page 191. Small specimens of European Sting Winkle have more stepped profile

Lifting up rocks on the lower shore will reveal a wide variety of living organisms, among which this species will often figure, crawling as rapidly as possible away from the light as soon as it is exposed. This species is markedly smaller and darker than the Netted Dog Whelk, H. *reticulata*, see page 191, and does not have such a net-like arrangement of grooves on its shell. If in real doubt, inspect the shape of the aperture, which is diagnostic. The eggs are laid in clusters rather than rows. This common species is found widely around the coasts of Europe.

MOLLUSCS

Sea Hare
Aplysia punctata

ID FACT FILE

SIZE:
To 20 cm long,
but usually about
7 cm

DESCRIPTION:
Body bulky and
fleshy, gradually
widening from
head to rear, with
a pair of tubular
tentacles at the
front end and a
pair of shorter,
tentacle-like
rhinophores just
behind. Colour
very
variable, often
dark reddish-
brown, also
green, red,
purple or black,
often mottled or
blotched

HABITAT:
At certain
seasons all up
the shore, in
pools; otherwise
offshore

LOOKALIKES:
A. fasciata and *A.
depilans* have
more pointed
rear ends and
are much rarer

Sea Hares are named after the resemblance of
their tentacles to floppy hare's ears. Most of a
Sea Hare's life is spent in deeper water
offshore, but in spring and summer large
numbers may come inshore to lay their long
strings of orange or pink eggs. Numerous
adults may also be found grazing on Sea
Lettuce, *Ulva lactuca*, see page 11, in rock
pools quite high on the shore, swimming with
languid undulations of the wing-like lobes that
run along either side of the body. This is a
widespread species, found all around the coasts
of Europe.

MOLLUSCS

| J | F | M | A | M | J |
| J | A | S | O | N | D |

Yellow-plumed Sea Slug
Berthella plumula

ID FACT FILE

SIZE:
To 6 cm long

DESCRIPTION:
Body yellow,
forming a convex
blob of yellow
jelly when out of
water, extruding
broad plume-like
'wings' in water.
Head with pair of
tentacles. Shell
present internally

HABITAT:
Lower shore, on
rock

LOOKALIKES:
B. citrina is much
smaller, to 7 mm
long

This species, found around all European
coasts, is most likely to be first noticed as a
rather puzzling yellow blob attached beneath a
dripping wet rock overhang or fixed to the
underside of a stone at low tide. Only by
gently detaching this blob and putting it in
water will the true nature of the beast be
revealed, as shown in the accompanying
illustration in which the tentacles on the head
are visible on the left-hand side. Its food
consists of compound sea squirts such as
Botryllus schlosseri.

J	F	M	A	M	J
J	A	S	O	N	D

MOLLUSCS

Orange-clubbed Sea Slug

Limacea clavigera

ID FACT FILE

SIZE:
To 18 mm long

DESCRIPTION:
Ground colour
white, with yellow
or orange
patterning. Body
rather elongated,
head fairly broad
with a fringe of
long feathery
tentacle-like
lobes, which also
occur at more
widely spaced
intervals along
the sides of the
body

HABITAT:
Lower shore, on
rocks

LOOKALIKES:
None on shore

This is one of the prettiest sea slugs found on
the shore, although several larger species with
spectacular orange markings are found in
deeper water. Despite its bright colours, this
species is surprisingly difficult to find and
usually only turns up after careful searching
among rocks and seaweeds at low water of
spring tides. As with all sea slugs, it needs to
be in water in order to appreciate its beauty,
otherwise it is just a heap of jelly. It feeds on
encrusting bryozoans and is distributed around
the coasts of Europe.

MOLLUSCS

A Sea Slug
Palio nothus

ID FACT FILE

SIZE:
1–2 cm long

DESCRIPTION:
Body rather slender, blackish-green with numerous pale flecks. Tubercles on top of the mantle conical in shape

HABITAT:
Lower shore

LOOKALIKES:
P. dubia is very similar, often larger (to 29 mm), very pale brownish-green, not flecked and not found on the shore

This small sea slug is only likely to be found by searching beneath stones, on the lowermost part of the shore, during the lowest of the spring tides. Like all the smaller sea slugs, it is very inconspicuous and contracts into a barely recognisable blob of jelly when out of water. Very careful searching or a good eye are therefore essential. The normal prey for this species, which occurs widely around the coasts of Europe, consists of *Bowerbankia* bryozoans. The spawn is often easier to find, forming a coiled white or pink ribbon.

MOLLUSCS

J	F	M	A	M	J
J	A	S	O	N	D

Sea Lemon
Archidoris pseudoargus

ID FACT FILE

Size:
To 12 cm long

Description:
Body elongated
oval, yellow,
sometimes
blotched darker,
with just a single
pair of tentacles
at the front end
and a tuft of gills
forming a rosette
on top of the
body towards the
rear end

Habitat:
Middle and lower
shore, on rocks

Lookalikes:
*Jorunna
tomentosa* paler,
always mottled
with brown, body
narrower

This common species found off all European
coasts is seldom discovered in water as
depicted in the accompanying illustration.
Most often it is found fixed firmly beneath a
stone or damp, overhanging rock face at low
tide, usually on or close to its food, comprising
various sponges, especially the Breadcrumb
Sponge, *Halichondria panicea*, see page 96.
When out of water the body forms a compact
hump but is not jelly-like as in most other sea
slugs, but rather is quite firm and rough, and
the rosette of gills is clearly visible.

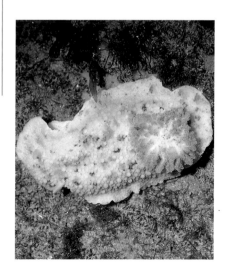

MOLLUSCS

J	F	M	A	M	J
J	A	S	O	N	D

Common Grey Sea Slug
Aeolidia papillosa

ID FACT FILE

SIZE:
To 12 cm long

DESCRIPTION:
Body elongated, grey to purplish-brown, tapering from front to rear and covered along both sides with a mass of thick hair-like structures called cerata, leaving just a bare line down the middle of the back.Top of head has white patches

HABITAT:
Middle and lower shore, under rocks and in pools

LOOKALIKES:
Aeolidiella glauca is smaller, with shorter, denser cerata and no white on the head

When submerged this large and common species, found around all European coasts, looks as though it is covered with fur. It feeds on a wide variety of sea anemones and so is often found near where they occur. In spring and summer you may turn over a rock and have the pleasure of discovering a specimen beside its long, coiled string of pinkish-purple eggs, as depicted in the illustration. These egg masses can be quite a common sight beneath rocks on the lower shore, but the slug is only rarely present.

MOLLUSCS

A Sea Slug
Hypselodoris villafranca

ID FACT FILE

SIZE:
To 3.5 cm long

DESCRIPTION:
Body is a beautiful blue, streaked with pale orange, fairly long and narrow, with a pair of short, thick oral tentacles on the head. Eight leaf-like gills on top of body near rear

HABITAT:
In pools on lower shore

LOOKALIKES:
H. tricolor is much broader, with eleven gills and fewer orange streaks

This spectacular species is found from the Atlantic coast of France southwards, but is unfortunately not present in the British Isles. Although usually found offshore, at certain times it can be found quite easily in rock pools on the lower shore. It belongs to a family of slugs, all of which secrete unpleasant defensive chemicals and are beautifully coloured but most of which are found only in tropical waters. It feeds solely on the sponge *Disidea fragilis*. Several other blue species are found in the Mediterranean.

MOLLUSCS

| J | F | M | A | M | J |
| J | A | S | O | N | D |

Celtic Sea Slug

Onchidella celtica

ID FACT FILE

SIZE:
To 12 mm long

DESCRIPTION:
Body dark
brownish,
greenish or
blackish, covered
with a dense
coat of wart-like
protruberances.
Head with a pair
of short
tentacles

HABITAT:
Upper and
middle shores

LOOKALIKES:
None

This very distinctive species is rather rare in
the British Isles, being restricted to Cornwall,
although on the continental mainland it is
found all down the Atlantic coast. Where it
does occur it can be extremely abundant and
conspicuous. As the tide recedes hundreds or
even thousands of animals may be seen
crawling around on the seaweed-covered rocks
as they become exposed. It follows the tide
down the shore as it recedes, feeding on the
seaweeds, especially the 'browns' on which it is
very well camouflaged.

MOLLUSCS

Common Saddle Oyster

Anomia ephippium

J	F	M	A	M	J
J	A	S	O	N	D

ID FACT FILE

SIZE:
To 6 cm across

DESCRIPTION:
Shell very flat, rather brittle, pinkish-white or greyish, often with a bluish tint, generally with a pearly gleam, covered with a series of wavy ridges

HABITAT:
Mainly on rocks, also on other molluscs and large seaweed holdfasts on the lower shore

LOOKALIKES:
The Prickly Saddle Oyster, *Heteranomia squamula* is smaller (usually no more than 12 mm across) and smoother

Saddle oysters are bivalve molluscs, having two parts (or valves) to the shell, connected by a hinge which allows the two valves to open. These are the flattest of all bivalves and scarcely protrude above the surface of the rocks to which they are firmly attached. This species is usually found in ones or twos, but Prickly Saddle Oysters often almost cover the undersides of stones, gleaming like fish scales in the sun when the stone is lifted to reveal them. The Prickly Saddle Oyster is a western species in Britain, while the Common Saddle Oyster is found all round our shores; both species are widespread on Continental coasts.

MOLLUSCS

J	F	M	A	M	J
J	A	S	O	N	D

Common Mussel
Mytilus edulis

ID FACT FILE

SIZE:
Length to
10 cm

DESCRIPTION:
Shell
elongate-oval,
tapering towards
the straight and
rather pointed
end (umbone)
that is nearest
the attachment
to the substrate.
Colour dark
bluish-grey to
purple, much
paler when dry.
Edge of mantle
light yellow-brown

HABITAT:
On rocks from
middle shore
downwards

LOOKALIKES:
In *M.
galloprovincialis*
the umbone is
curved
downwards; the
Bearded Mussel,
*Modiolus
barbatus* is
bristly

On exposed rocky shores the Common Mussel
forms massive beds containing millions of
individuals, so densely packed that it is
impossible to find a space between them and
their shells become distorted. They are well
able to withstand the pounding of the winter
storms because of their very firm attachment
to the rocks via so-called byssus threads, which
pass out from between the two halves of the
shell and can be renewed as necessary.
Economically this is a very important species
that is widely eaten, being abundant around
the coasts of Europe.

MOLLUSCS

J	F	M	A	M	J
J	A	S	O	N	D

Great Scallop

Pecten maximus

ID FACT FILE

SIZE:
Shell to 15 cm
across

DESCRIPTION:
Bivalve,
right-hand valve
convex on top,
left-hand valve
flattened. Each
valve with up to
17 radiating ribs
having a rounded
profile. Colour of
shell pinkish

HABITAT:
Just below
normal extreme
low-water mark
of spring tides

LOOKALIKES:
Other scallops,
but this is the
biggest

This large species usually lives just offshore
where normal low spring tides do not quite
reach, but in some years exceptionally low
tides in March and April may leave a few
specimens high and dry, as seen in the
illustration. When exposed on land the scallop
may open the two valves of its shell to reveal
the mantle with its rows of black eyes, which in
this species are rather small. They are seen
more easily when the scallop is submerged.
This species has been depleted by overfishing
over most of its range, which takes in all coasts.

| J | F | M | A | M | J |
| J | A | S | O | N | D |

Queen Scallop
Aequipecten opercularis

ID FACT FILE

SIZE:
To 9 cm across

DESCRIPTION:
Shell oval, pale
brown, with one
valve more
convex than the
other, with a
radiating fan
of 20 very
prominent ridges
paralleled by
numerous
grooves, giving
the edge of the
shell a deeply
scalloped
appearance

HABITAT:
Lower shore and
below

LOOKALIKES:
See other
scallops

This attractive scallop, present on all coasts,
mainly lives offshore, but is sometimes found
on the lowest part of the shore exposed during
spring tides. Even then, it may be present one
day, and then when the same shore is revisited
during the next low tides a month later, there
is no sign of even a single specimen. The
juveniles are attached to rocks by byssus
threads, but the adults swim well, clapping
their shell valves together to make quite rapid
forward progress. The eyes on the mantle are
prominent when the valves are gaping open.

MOLLUSCS

| J | F | M | A | M | J |
| J | A | S | O | N | D |

Variegated Scallop

Chlamys varia

ID FACT FILE

SIZE:
To 6 cm long

DESCRIPTION:
Shell
reddish-brown,
often marked
with black, each
valve having
25–35
pronounced
ridges beset with
spines. Ears on
shell prominent,
much larger on
one side than on
the other

HABITAT:
Free living and
on rocks on
lower shore

LOOKALIKES:
See other
scallops

This species is most often found attached by
strong byssus threads beneath a rock on the
lower shore. It has a complicated sex life, first
becoming mature as a male, but then
swapping from male to female several times
throughout its life. Breeding takes place during
the warmer months from spring to autumn.
This is a very widespread species, found on all
European coasts and fished commercially in
some areas. Scallop shells are also often used
as ornaments.

Common or Flat Oyster

Ostrea edulis

J	F	M	A	M	J
J	A	S	O	N	D

ID FACT FILE

SIZE:
To about
10 cm across

DESCRIPTION:
Shell flat, dull
grey, very
variable in
shape, oval,
pear-shaped
or circular,
extremely rough
and covered with
a scaly
concentric series
of radiating
ridges

HABITAT:
Lower shore, on
coarse muddy
and gravelly
bottoms and
attached to rocks

LOOKALIKES:
Portuguese
Oyster,
Crassostrea gigas
is more narrowly
oval with large
jagged, scaly
ridges

Natural populations of this highly regarded
delicacy have declined considerably in recent
years, and it is now quite rare in many areas
and extinct in others. In localities that are
particularly favourable for its development it is
cultured commercially. Although the outside
of the shell is rough and ugly, the inner surface
is smooth and glossy, the well-known 'mother
of pearl'. Breeding occurs between May and
August, when the oysters become temporarily
inedible. They feed on green planktonic algae
and are widespread but scattered around the
coasts of Europe.

MOLLUSCS

Common Cockle
Cerastoderma edule

J	F	M	A	M	J
J	A	S	O	N	D

ID FACT FILE

SIZE:
To 5 cm long

DESCRIPTION:
Shell thick and deep, pale brown, broadly oval and with 24 broad ribs crossed at right-angles by a series of concentric ridges which may have a few short, flattened spines

HABITAT:
In sand on lower shore

LOOKALIKES:
There are many other similar species

Although usually spending its life buried at a shallow depth in sand and fine gravel, from where it is raked out by commercial cockle fishers on a large scale, individual specimens may also be found on the surface during unusually low tides, as in the illustration. In flat, sheltered bays numbers may reach astronomical proportions, with juveniles settling down on the sand in densities of as much as 10,000 per square meter. This is an abundant species around the coasts of northern Europe, although empty shells are most often found, rather than live animals.

MOLLUSCS

| J | F | M | A | M | J |
| J | A | S | O | N | D |

Brown Venus

Callista chione

ID FACT FILE

SIZE:
To 9 cm long

DESCRIPTION:
Shell broadly
oval, fairly deep,
smooth and
glossy, rich
reddish-brown,
with a series of
very fine
concentric lines
and distinct
growth bands.
Siphon short

HABITAT:
Extreme lower
shore, on sand
between rocks

LOOKALIKES:
None

This superb and very attractive, impressively
large species is unfortunately rather rare,
being found only in southwest England and
the Channel Islands southwards to the
Mediterranean. It is such a splendid species
that it is worth making the effort to find it,
although on no account should live specimens
be collected. In some books it is cited as living
only below the lowest tides, in the sublittoral,
but on some Cornish shores it is easy to find
numbers of living specimens exposed by
normal low spring tides.

MOLLUSCS

Rayed Artemis
Dosinia exoleta

J F M A M J
J A S O N D

ID FACT FILE

SIZE:
To 6 cm across

DESCRIPTION:
Shell very deep
and almost
circular, with
small umbones
projecting at
hinged end,
covered in a fine
concentric
pattern of closely
spaced ridges
and well-marked
growth stages.
Colour variable,
often pale brown

HABITAT:
Lower shore, on
coarse muddy
sand and gravel

LOOKALIKES:
There are several
similar-looking
species

This is perhaps the most handsome of several
similar-looking species found on the lower
shore on muddy sand and gravel and differing
in size, shell shape and depth, colour and a
number of small structural details of the shell
that take considerable experience to master
fully. Once known, most of the commoner
species can be identified on sight, although
empty shells are found more often than living
animals, which are only likely to be exposed
during low spring tides. Like all bivalves, this is
a filter-feeder. It is present on all coasts.

MOLLUSCS

Banded Venus
Clausinella fasciata

ID FACT FILE

Size:
Shell up to
2.5 cm long

Description:
Shell forming an
imperfect
triangle, each
valve rather flat
and bearing 15
somewhat broad
and rounded
concentric
ridges. Colour
variable, often
warm rusty
brown, usually
with darker
radiating bands

Habitat:
In sand on lower
shore and
sublittoral

Lookalikes:
Striped Venus,
Chamelea gallina
is up to 4 cm
long, with three
broad radiating
chestnut bands
on a pale
background

As with all the bivalves that dwell out of sight
within sand, this species is mostly seen as
empty shells lying on the surface. However, on
very low tides living specimens are often
stranded on the surface, as depicted in the
illustration. This widespread species is much
smaller than some of the other common
bivalves of sandy shores, but very distinctive
and handsome. It occurs on shores that are
not too exposed to strong wave action.

MOLLUSCS

Banded Wedge Shell

Donax vittatus

ID FACT FILE

SIZE:
Shell to 38 mm
long

DESCRIPTION:
Shell forming an
imperfect and
elongated
triangle, each
valve of similar
size and shape,
varied in colour,
from pinkish-
white to deep
gold

HABITAT:
In sand on
lower shore

LOOKALIKES:
See Thin Tellin,
Angulus tenuis,
page 212

The Banded Wedge Shell lives on moderately
exposed or even exposed sandy shores all
round the coasts of Europe. Shells from dead
animals are often cast up at the top of the
beach, but to see the living animal, as depicted
in the illustration, you will need to follow the
receding tide, when a few live specimens may
be stranded on the surface of the sand. Wedge
shells are well-adapted for burrowing in sand,
and can rapidly retreat downwards to avoid
being swept up on shore by the pounding surf.

MOLLUSCS

Thin Tellin
Angulus tenuis

ID FACT FILE

SIZE:
To 28 mm long

DESCRIPTION:
Shell a rather
irregular oval
shape, rather
thin, flat and
brittle, with the
front margin
broadly rounded
and the rear one
tapered and with
an abrupt angle.
Colour and
degree of
banding very
varied

HABITAT:
In sand on lower
shore

LOOKALIKES:
There are several
similar species,
such as Banded
Wedge Shell,
Donax vittatus,
see page 211,
but none nearly
so common as
this one

Because they live in a shallow burrow in fine
silty sand, living specimens of the Thin Tellin
are rarely seen, although they may be found on
the surface of the sand during an exceptionally
low tide, as in the specimen illustrated. By
contrast, you are likely to encounter thousands
of shells from dead individuals scattered
around on sandy shores around all the
European coasts, evidence of the sheer
numbers present beneath your feet. Two
long siphons are extended for feeding and
respiration when the animal is buried in
the sand.

MOLLUSCS

Pod Razor Shell

Ensis siliqua

J	F	M	A	M	J
J	A	S	O	N	D

ID FACT FILE

SIZE:
To 20 cm long,
2 cm wide

DESCRIPTION:
Shell long and
narrow, pod-
shaped, blunt at
one end, convex
at the other,
brownish, very
slightly curved

HABITAT:
In sand on lower
shore

LOOKALIKES:
Common Razor
Shell, *E. ensis* is
much smaller
(to 13 cm) and
more curved. In
E. arcuatus (to
15 cm) one shell
margin is curved,
the other almost
straight

Razor shells live in deep, permanent burrows in the sand. The specimen illustrated was dug out in order to be photographed and to show what is down below in thousands as you walk across the sand of the lower shore. Razor shells dig very rapidly into the sand using their powerful muscular foot, enabling them to disappear downwards within seconds. At high tide they move nearer the surface of the sand and protrude a short siphon for feeding (by filtration) and breathing. This species is common on all coasts and like all razor shells is badly over-collected for food and bait.

MOLLUSCS

Sandhill Snail
Theba pisana

ID FACT FILE

SIZE:
Shell 9–20 mm high, 12–25 mm across

DESCRIPTION:
Shell subglobular, with 5–6 slightly convex whorls. Mouth elliptical, with an internal rib. Shell mainly white or very pale brown, usually with a spiral pattern of darker brown bands, usually broken up into spots

HABITAT:
Sand dunes and top of sandy shores

LOOKALIKES:
Several similar species but not aggregating like this one

This is not a snail that you are likely to find as a solitary, lonesome specimen. Instead, its sheer numbers are most likely to grab your attention, as wherever it occurs it normally builds up into large populations which spend periods of dry weather fixed en masse to vegetation such as Sea Holly, Sea Spurge and Marram Grass. This Mediterranean species has been introduced into many sandy habitats along the Atlantic coast of Europe. In the British Isles it was introduced near St Ives in Cornwall in about 1797 and has since spread as far as Wales.

BRYOZOANS

J	F	M	A	M	J
J	A	S	O	N	D

ID FACT FILE

SIZE:
Mat to 3 cm or
more across

DESCRIPTION:
A flat minutely
bristly greyish-
silver sheet,
mainly on various
seaweeds, also
on rocks and
mollusc shells.
The sheet is
composed of
numerous
individual zooids
up to 0.5 mm
long

HABITAT:
Lower shore

LOOKALIKES:
*Membranipora
membranacea* is
not spiny and is
almost restricted
to blades of
Laminaria kelps

Sea Mat

Electra pilosa

Sea Mats resemble very fine, miniature sheets of bubble-wrap polythene attached to sea-weeds. This species is most often found on Toothed Wrack, Carragheen and Grapeweed. Sea Mats are bryozoans (Phylum Bryozoa) and form immobile colonies of various forms. The colonies are composed of numerous individual zooids, each of which has a fan of tentacles which are used for feeding and retract rapidly when disturbed. In water, Sea Mats have a slightly furry appearance due to the masses of tentacles. This is one of the commonest species on all shores.

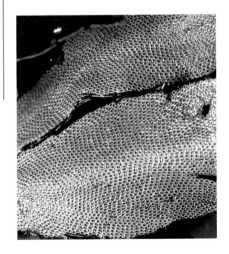

ECHINODERMS

Sand Star

Astropecten irregularis

ID FACT FILE

SIZE:
To 20 cm across

DESCRIPTION:
Body fairly rigid,
pale pinkish-
orange, with five
arms edged with
numerous
marginal plates.
Upper surface
rough to the
touch, covered in
numerous tiny
tubercles. Tube
feet pointed and
lacking suckers
at the tips

HABITAT:
In sand on lower
shore

LOOKALIKES:
See other
starfish (but no
others live in
sand)

Although normally living in sand, this species
has the habit of hauling itself out onto the
surface as the tide is coming in, and then
moves down the shore by flopping over and
over. It can also tiptoe its way quite rapidly
across flat sand on its numerous tube feet,
which project from the underside of the arms,
as in other starfish. Its range of food is wide
and includes bivalve molluscs such as cockles,
worms, brittle stars and various crustaceans.
This is a widespread species found around all
the coasts of Europe.

ECHINODERMS

J	F	M	A	M	J
J	A	S	O	N	D

Common Cushion Star
Asterina gibbosa

ID FACT FILE

SIZE:
To 5 cm across

DESCRIPTION:
Shape a regular
pentagon. Arms
short. Upper
surface usually
grey, also
greenish or
brownish,
sometimes
mottled, covered
with groups of
short, stiff
spines and thus
rough to the
touch

HABITAT:
Lower shore, on
and under rocks
and seaweeds

LOOKALIKES:
A. phylactica
smaller, to just
15 mm across,
with a star-like
central pattern

On many shores this is the easiest starfish to
find and the most abundant, often being found
clinging to the undersides of stones. Unlike
most other starfish, which are predators, this is
a scavenger, mopping up decaying material of
both animal and plant origin. It becomes
mature as a male when two years old, then at
four it changes to a female and remains as one
for the succeeding three years or so of its
remaining life. Eggs are attached to rocks and
emerge as juveniles. Distribution is wide, but
excludes the eastern Channel and North Sea.

ECHINODERMS

J	F	M	A	M	J
J	A	S	O	N	D

Common Starfish
Asterias rubens

ID FACT FILE

SIZE:
To 50 cm

DESCRIPTION:
Body thick
and tough,
strengthened
with a mesh-like
internal skeleton,
pale orange,
covered with
numerous broad
whitish spines.
Arms five, fairly
stout. Tube feet
armed with
suckers at their
tips

HABITAT:
Lower shore and
offshore, on
rocks, sand and
gravel

LOOKALIKES:
*Henricia
sanguineolenta*
has longer,
slimmer arms
and is bright
purplish-red;
Luidia ciliaris is
pale brownish-
orange and has
seven long arms

Although most common offshore, this
ubiquitous (in Europe) species can be
abundant on the lower part of the shore
exposed only during spring tides. Individuals
missing one or more arms, or in a partial state
of regeneration, are common. The ability to
regenerate lost arms is found in all starfish, and
even a single arm can grow into the complete
animal. In this species males and females are
separate and the eggs hatch as swimming
larvae which join the plankton. Food is varied,
including molluscs such as mussels, as well as
other starfish.

ECHINODERMS

Spiny Starfish
Marthasterias glacialis

J	F	M	A	M	J
J	A	S	O	N	D

ID FACT FILE

SIZE:
To 70 cm across

DESCRIPTION:
Body very large, heavily built and leathery, with five long, tapering arms almost covered in numerous conspicuous thick, sharp spines set in neat longitudinal rows. Colour variable, often a beautiful shade of purple, also white, grey, green, yellow or red

HABITAT:
Lower shore, on coarse gravel and sand, often among rocks

LOOKALIKES:
None

In both size and form this is a spectacular starfish and the purple-tinted varieties are particularly beautiful. To see it you will have to visit the shore during a spring tide, as only then will the water be low enough to expose the exciting variety of organisms living on the lowermost part of the shore. The favourite prey for the Spiny Starfish is the Common Starfish, *Asterias rubens*, see opposite, but it also feeds on other species of starfish, crabs and a variety of molluscs such as mussels and cockles. Distrubution is wide, but excludes the southern North Sea and eastern Channel.

Common Brittle-star

Ophiothrix fragilis

ID FACT FILE

SIZE:
Disc to 2 cm
across, arms to
7 cm long

DESCRIPTION:
Body consists of
a central disc
from which
radiate five long,
slender arms
(but thicker than
in most other
brittle-stars).
Arms divided into
many segments,
each of which
bears seven
spines on each
side. Colour very
variable

HABITAT:
Lower shore,
under rocks and
on coarse sand
and gravel

LOOKALIKES:
Other brittle-
stars, none
common on
shore

This is the only brittle-star likely to be found
between tidemarks on all European shores. It
can be quite abundant beneath stones and in
rock pools on the lower shore. Its colour is
fantastically variable, often just plain dull
brown, and the form illustrated is probably the
most striking of all. The arms break off very
easily and are used in feeding, being raised
vertically to trap food particles in the water
using the numerous tube feet. Breeding
occurs during the summer and the larvae
are planktonic.

ECHINODERMS

Purple-tipped or Green Sea Urchin

Psammechinus miliaris

J	F	M	A	M	J
J	A	S	O	N	D

ID FACT FILE

SIZE:
To 5 cm across

DESCRIPTION:
Body (called a test) a slightly flattened sphere, densely covered in rather short glossy spines that are tipped with a beautiful shade of deep purple. Tube feet issuing from plates on underside

HABITAT:
Lower shore, beneath stones

LOOKALIKES:
Paracentrotus lividus lives in deep cavities in soft rocks; in *Sphaerechinus granularis* the spines are denser and white-tipped (not British)

This is by far the most common sea urchin found between tidemarks. To see it you will need to look beneath stones on the lower shore during a spring tide. It is easy to miss, as it is frequently covered with bits of broken shell and seaweed, which act as camouflage. The colour is variable, and the intensity of the purple on the tips of the spines is not always pronounced. Some specimens appear pinkish-brown. This species, which is common throughout our region, feeds on a huge variety of items, including young barnacles, immature molluscs and seaweeds.

J	F	M	A	M	J
J	A	S	O	N	D

Edible Sea Urchin

Echinus esculentus

ID FACT FILE

SIZE:
To 18 cm across

DESCRIPTION:
Body
dome-shaped,
with a flattened
underside, bright
pink, covered in
long red spines
having white
bases and violet
tips

HABITAT:
Mainly just below
the lowest
tidemark,
occasionally just
within it

LOOKALIKES:
Nothing of this
size and colour
likely to be found
between
tidemarks

Although the very ornamental empty tests are
unfortunately often found for sale at the
seaside, the living animal is seldom seen,
although it can be quite abundant on some
shores at low tide, especially in springtime.
Once seen, its large size and beautiful colour
make it impossible to confuse with any other
sea urchin found between tidemarks. It feeds
by grazing on the blades of seaweeds such as
kelps and on bryozoans such as the Sea Mats
that live on them. It is found around the coasts
of Europe except for the Mediterranean.

ECHINODERMS

Sea Potato
Echinocardium cordatum

J	F	M	A	M	J
J	A	S	O	N	D

ID FACT FILE

SIZE:
Up to 9 cm long

DESCRIPTION:
Body rather
flattened, heart-
shaped,
bilaterally
symmetrical on
either side of a
line down the
middle of the
long axis,
covered in a
dense pelt of
yellow spines

HABITAT:
In sand from
middle shore
downwards

LOOKALIKES:
*Spatangus
purpureus* is
similar shape
but bright purple;
E. pennatifidum
is yellowish but
almost circular
in outline

As this virtually cosmopolitan species lives in a
burrow about 15 cm deep in the sand it will
not normally be seen unless it is dug out.
However, after severe storms thousands may
be cast up on the strandline. It belongs to a
group of sea urchins called heart urchins on
account of their shape. Instead of being in the
middle of the underside, as in other sea
urchins, the mouth is situated towards its front
end and is used to feed on detritus in the sand.
This is collected by the tube feet from within
the burrow and from around the breathing
channel where it opens onto the surface.

ECHINODERMS

J	F	M	A	M	J
J	A	S	O	N	D

Cotton-spinner
Holothuria forskali

ID FACT FILE

SIZE:
To 20 cm or
more long, to
4 cm wide

DESCRIPTION:
Body long
and fleshy,
resembling a
coarse, rather
blunt prickly
black cucumber.
Underside pale,
covered with
masses of tube
feet

LOOKALIKES:
None of same
colour or
between
tidemarks

Not surprisingly in view of its appearance, this
strange creature belongs to a group of animals
known as sea cucumbers. These belong to the
class Holothurioidea, included along with the
sea urchins and starfish in the Phylum
echinodermata. There is a mouth at the front
end, which in many species is surrounded by
branching tentacles that can quickly be
retracted. Sea cucumbers feed on suspended
matter in the water or deposited on the sand.
This species gets its common name from its
habit, when handled, of squirting out a mass of
sticky white, cotton-like threads. It occurs from
the south and west coasts of Britain and
Ireland southwards to the Mediterranean.

ECHINODERMS

Sea Gherkin
Pawsonia saxicola

J	F	M	A	M	J
J	A	S	O	N	D

ID FACT FILE

Size:
To 15 cm long,
2 cm wide

Description:
Body fairly long
and narrow, skin
very smooth and
white, often
mottled with
random pale
pinkish blotches.
Tentacles long
and branched,
black

Habitat:
Lower shore

Lookalikes:
None

The Sea Gherkin is quite common underneath stones, jammed into rock crevices or in large old kelp holdfasts. It just occurs on the lower shore so only a low spring tide will expose its habitat. When out of water the crown of branching, twig-like black tentacles is normally withdrawn into the body (as in illustration). If you immerse the stone in water you may see the tentacles gradually extend (but eventually replace the stone exactly as you found it). Distribution is from the south and west coasts of the British Isles southwards to the Mediterranean.

SEA SQUIRT

Light-bulb Sea Squirt
Clavelina lepadiformis

ID FACT FILE

SIZE:
To 20 mm high,
4 mm across

DESCRIPTION:
Forming clumps
of flask-like
individuals each
linked at its base
to a common
stem attached to
rock and large
seaweed. Colour
transparent
except for a
silvery ring
around the apex
and a stripe
down the side

HABITAT:
Lower shore,
usually on rocks

SEASON:
March–October,
dying back in
winter

LOOKALIKES:
None

Clumps composed of 20 or more individuals of this very distinctive sea squirt can be quite common on the lower shore on all rocky coasts, but also sometimes occur in rock pools on the middle shore. When out of water they just collapse into a shapeless mass of jelly, and their full shape and beauty can only be appreciated when they are submerged. Sea squirts feed and breathe by drawing water in through one end and expelling it out the other after food particles and oxygen have been extracted from it.

SEA SQUIRT

J	F	M	A	M	J
J	A	S	O	N	D

Gooseberry Sea Squirt

Dendrodoa grossularia

ID FACT FILE

SIZE:
To 2 cm long

DESCRIPTION:
Solitary or
in small
unconnected
groups, pinkish-
red, resembling a
miniature
volcanic cone
with a thick rim
and broad base

HABITAT:
Lower shore

LOOKALIKES:
See Redcurrant
Sea Squirt,
*Distomus
variolosus*,
page 228

This attractive brightly coloured sea squirt is
widely distributed around all European
coastlines, and it is often common in estuaries
where salinity is reduced. It is usually attached
in small groups to rocks, stones, shells or large
old kelp holdfasts, as illustrated here.
Unlike the Light-bulb Sea Squirt, *Clavelina
lepadiformis*, see opposite, which is very soft
and bag-like, the body of this species is quite
leathery and hard. As in all ascidians, each
individual is a hermaphrodite, containing both
male and female reproductive organs.

SEA SQUIRT

J	F	M	A	M	J
J	A	S	O	N	D

Redcurrant Sea Squirt
Distomus variolosus

ID FACT FILE

SIZE:
To 10 mm long,
5 mm across

DESCRIPTION:
Forming masses
of closely packed
bright red
individual ovoid
tests, each
supplied with
its own paired
siphons but
all linked
communally
to a shared
encrusting base

HABITAT:
Lower shore

LOOKALIKES:
See Gooseberry
Sea Squirt,
*Dendrodoa
grossularia*,
page 227

The conspicuous bright red colonies of this
sea squirt are mostly likely to be noticed
encrusting the broad stems of kelps such as
Oarweed, *Laminaria digitata*, see page 14,
which are exposed during a low spring tide.
Large sheets are rapidly built up through a
very efficient process of asexual budding
carried out by the individuals already present.
This enables populations to build up very
rapidly during the warmer summer months.
Sedentary tunicates such as these have free-
swimming tadpole-like larvae. This species is
found from southwest England and western
Ireland southwards to the Mediterranean.

SEA SQUIRT

Argus Sea Squirt
Morchellium argus

J	F	M	A	M	J
J	A	S	O	N	D

ID FACT FILE

SIZE:
To 4 cm long

DESCRIPTION:
Forming
elongated,
pinkish-orange
colonies hanging
from rocks.
Each zooid is
long and slender,
each having an
oral siphon with
eight lobes

HABITAT:
Lower shore, on
rock

LOOKALIKES:
*Aplidium
proliferum* is
pinkish-red,
squat and
flat-topped, not
hanging and
occurs in the
open on rocks
and stones

This is one of several rather puzzling 'blobby things' found beneath dripping wet rock overhangs at low water of spring tides. Once out of water, several different kinds of soft-bodied creatures can look confusingly like amorphous blobs of jelly, leaving the beginner with more questions than answers about identities. In this species the individual zooids are packed inside a sac-like outer envelope that hangs down from rocks in clusters of long narrow pinkish lobes. Although often abundant locally, this species is restricted to the west and southwest coasts of the British Isles, southwards to Brittany.

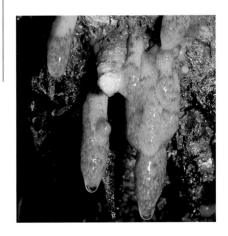

SEA SQUIRT

J	F	M	A	M	J
J	A	S	O	N	D

Star Ascidian
Botryllus schlosseri

ID FACT FILE

Size:
Forming sheets to 10 cm or more across

Description:
Forming broad, flat, thin jelly-like sheets that are composed of numerous embedded zooids in a star-like pattern. Colour most often blue, also gold, green, red or orange

Habitat:
Lower shore, on rocks, stones, shells and large seaweeds

Lookalikes:
Botrylloides leachi is composed of zooids arranged in parallel chains (see top left in illustration)

This spectacular ascidian is common around the coasts of Europe. Although most often dark blue, as illustrated (the yellowish chain at top left is *Botrylloides leachi*) this species shows enormous variation in colour and in some areas orange is the commonest form. Each of the 'stars' within the jelly-like sheet is composed of several individual zooids arranged around a central shared exhalant opening. By contrast, each zooid has its own individual mouth opening. Although usually flat and sheet-like, colonies may also form deeper, fleshier mounds.

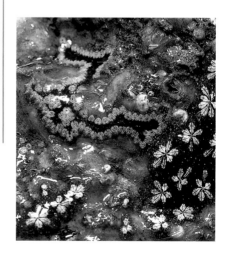

FISH

Mermaid's Purse

J	F	M	A	M	J
J	A	S	O	N	D

ID FACT FILE

SIZE:
5–10 cm long,
2–5 cm broad

DESCRIPTION:
Olive brown or
blackish, rather
translucent when
fresh, black
when old, spikes
or tendrils on
each of the four
corners

HABITAT:
Found on lower
shore or cast up
on shore

LOOKALIKES:
None

Mermaid's Purses are the egg capsules of
certain widespread non-bony fish, which
include sharks, skates, rays and dogfish. These
are deep-water fish, not found on the shore,
and all the fish on the following pages are
bony fish. The Mermaid's Purses illustrated
below were made by a dogfish, probably the
Lesser Spotted Dogfish, *Scyliorhynus canicu-
lus*, and were exposed on a low spring tide. The
cases are attached to seaweeds by the coiling
tendrils at each corner. In rays and skates the
egg capsule is broader and has a long spike on
each corner.

FISH

J	F	M	A	M	J
J	A	S	O	N	D

Dab
Limanda limanda

ID FACT FILE

SIZE:
Up to 40 cm long

DESCRIPTION:
Body flat, broadly
oval, sand-
coloured, with a
few darker spots,
with both eyes
on upper
surface. Skin
feels rough to
the touch due to
fine teeth along
the upper edges.
Tail with convex
outer margin

HABITAT:
Sandy shores
and estuaries;
sandy rock pools

LOOKALIKES:
Flounder,
*Pleuronectes
flesus* has
square-cut tail
and smooth skin.

The Dab, found on all coasts, is a member
of the very distinctive flatfish family,
Pleuronectidae, whose members spend their
lives lying permanently on just one side. At an
early age one eye migrates around to join the
other on the side that is uppermost, which is
able to change colour very rapidly in order to
match and blend in with the background. The
underside is always very pale. Although the
Dab can reach a length of 40 cm, it is usually
far smaller, especially inshore where you are
most likely to find it.

FISH

| J | F | M | A | M | J |
| J | A | S | O | N | D |

Lesser Sand Eel
Ammodytes tobianus

ID FACT FILE

SIZE:
To 20 cm long

DESCRIPTION:
Body long and narrow, covered in very small scales, body greenish above, silvery white below, head pointed, lower jaw longer than the upper, which can be protruded to form a short proboscis

HABITAT:
Sandy bays, from middle shore downwards

LOOKALIKES:
Greater Sand Eel, *Hyperoplus lanceolatus* cannot protrude upper jaw into proboscis; conspicuous blackish spot in front of eye.

You are unlikely to find fully grown specimens of this fish on the shore, but shoals of juveniles (illustrated) can be quite common sweeping rapidly back and forth in large rock pools with sandy bottoms, especially around the bases of large rocks where the fish can seek cover. Adults are less conspicuous as they spend a great deal of their time immersed in sand. Found widely around the coasts of Europe, this is a very important item of food for seabirds and various larger fish, but over-fishing by man is now taking a serious toll.

J	F	M	A	M	J
J	A	S	O	N	D

Shanny
Lipophrys pholis

ID FACT FILE

SIZE:
To 13 cm long

DESCRIPTION:
Body elongated,
with blunt head,
tapering
gradually
backwards to
tail. Colour
speckled
brownish or
greenish, with
paler underside
and lips. A rather
faint dark spot
near front of
dorsal fin. No
tentacles on
head. Skin
soft and slimy,
lacking scales

HABITAT:
Among rocks,
stones and
seaweed at all
levels on most
shores

LOOKALIKES:
Montagu's
Blenny,
*Coryphoblennius
galerita* has crest
of fringed
tentacles
between eyes
(southwest
Britain to
northwest Africa)

This is probably the commonest fish on most
shores, and if you see a sudden spurt of
movement in a rock pool or even just a puff of
sand this will probably be the culprit. The
dorsal fin extends from just behind the head
almost as far as the tail fin. Although the colour
is usually an attractive camouflage pattern of
green, black and pale brown, males turn almost
black during the breeding season. The strong
teeth are used to bite barnacles and small
mussels off the rocks. This common species is
found on all coasts of northern Europe.

FISH

Five-bearded Rockling
Ciliata mustela

ID FACT FILE

SIZE:
To 20 cm long

DESCRIPTION:
Body long and slim, fairly slab-sided, dark brown, lighter on some backgrounds than others. Dorsal and then anal fin extending down last two-thirds of body as far as tail. Five barbels present on head

HABITAT:
In pools and under rocks on rocky shores

LOOKALIKES:
In Shore Rockling, *Gaidropsarus mediterraneus* and Three-bearded Rockling, *G. vulgaris* there are only three barbels

Although superficially rather eel-like this species, found on all coasts, can easily be identified as a rockling by the barbels which protrude from the head like miniature tentacles, one on the chin, two on the snout beside the nostrils and two more in front of the eyes. In the other two rocklings found on rocky shores in Europe only three barbels are present. Rocklings feed mainly on various smaller fishes and crustaceans such as shrimps. The eggs are shed into water and the larvae join the plankton.

FISH

Worm Pipefish
Nerophis lumbriciformis

ID FACT FILE

SIZE:
To 15 cm long

DESCRIPTION:
Body smooth,
more or less
circular in
outline, at its
thickest about
one-third of way
behind head,
tapering
gradually to a
point at the rear,
with a short
upturned snout.
Short dorsal fin
only fin present.
Colour dark
blackish-brown,
underside with
white lines or
dots

HABITAT:
Under stones
and weed on
lower shore

LOOKALIKES:
Deep-snouted
Pipefish,
*Syngnathus
typhle,* tail fin is
present, long
snout as broad
as head; in
Lesser Pipefish,
S. rostellatus
tail fin present
but long snout is
narrow

Pipefish are members of the same family as the
seahorses. The Worm Pipefish can sometimes
be abundant beneath stones and seaweeds on
rocky shores, although in the British Isles it is
restricted to coasts of the southwest and
Channel (and very rarely on North Sea coasts).
On the Continent it is found on Channel coasts
and then southwards to Gibraltar. Pipefish only
have tiny mouths, which open just far enough
to admit the tiny plankton on which they feed.
The body is remarkably rigid and they are
feeble swimmers.

FISH

J	F	M	A	M	J
J	A	S	O	N	D

Butterfish

Centronotus gunnellus

ID FACT FILE

SIZE:
To 25 cm

DESCRIPTION:
Body dark brown,
long and rather
eel-like, but high
and narrow in
section rather
than almost
round, with a
small rounded
head. Along
almost the entire
length of the
back runs a long
low dorsal fin
having a series
of 12 regularly
spaced black
spots with white
rims along its
base. Tail blunt

HABITAT:
Beneath stones
on the lower
shore

LOOKALIKES:
Eel-pout, *Zoarces
viviparus* has
bigger head,
pointed tail fin
and no black
spots on dorsal
fin

Try to pick up a Butterfish and you will immediately realise how it came by this name – it is as slippery as butter. This is because the scales are only tiny and are embedded in a very slimy and slippery skin. The Butterfish occurs widely on northern European coastlines, and is normally found by lifting large stones on the lower shore, as seen in the illustration. In the early part of the year you may be lucky enough to find a male tightly coiled around his neat clutch of yellow eggs.

FISH

J	F	M	A	M	J
J	A	S	O	N	D

Father Lasher
Myoxocephalus scorpius

ID FACT FILE

SIZE:
To 30 cm long

DESCRIPTION:
Body deep,
tapering off
rapidly towards
the rear end,
reddish-brown or
greyish, with
darker blotches.
Head rather big,
noticeably
flattened from
top to bottom,
adorned with
rather blunt
spines and bony
crests. Two
spines on gill
cover

HABITAT:
Rocky shores
and estuaries,
only found
between tide-
marks in north

LOOKALIKES:
Long-spined
Sea Scorpion,
Taurulus bubalis
has three spines
on gill cover and
one or two fleshy
tentacles at
corner of mouth

Although found widely around the coasts of
northern Europe, the Father Lasher is only
found between tidemarks in the north of its
range; further south (e.g. in southern England)
is only occurs offshore. It should be handled
with care, as there is a row of sharp spines
along the body which, although they do not
inject any poison, can cause nasty cuts that
seem very ready to become infected and
inflamed. There are two separate dorsal fins on
the back, which are quite tall when fully raised.

FISH

Rock Goby

Gobius paganellus

ID FACT FILE

SIZE:
To 12 cm long

DESCRIPTION:
Body reddish-brown, sometimes mottled greenish, fairly stout, tapering gradually towards rear tail fin which is quite deep. Dorsal fin in two sections, the front with fewer rays than the rear one. Pectoral fin (just behind gills) with a few free upper rays (no tissue between them)

HABITAT:
Rock pools

LOOKALIKES:
Other gobies

In gobies the dorsal fin is in two sections, unlike in the superficially similar blennies in which a single, long fin is present. The Rock Goby is only found on rocky shores, from the west of the British Isles to Channel coasts and southwards to the Mediterranean. In females there is a pale yellow upper margin to the front dorsal fin (in males this band is a much brighter yellow or orange). As in all gobies, the head is broad, the eyes bulging and the lips protruding. Gobies can be tricky to identify in the field, and sometimes where they occur is the most useful characteristic.

FISH

Common Goby
Pomatoschistes microps

ID FACT FILE

SIZE:
To 7 cm long

DESCRIPTION:
Two dorsal fins, well separated on top of back, which is rather flattish. Eyes bulging, situated well up on top of head. Colour very variable, usually blotched or speckled

HABITAT:
In pools on sandy shores and in creeks in saltmarshes

LOOKALIKES:
Sand Goby, *P. minutus* is mainly found offshore; male has dark blue spot on rear margin of front dorsal fin

Common Gobies are often present in large numbers in sandy pools exposed by the ebbing tide in estuaries and in sandy areas of rocky shores. When stationary the camouflaged colouring makes this fish very hard to spot against the sandy bottom, but the response to disturbance is to shoot rapidly away, when the previously unsuspected presence of many individuals is revealed. The female deposits her eggs beneath an upturned shell, where they are closely guarded by the male.

FISH

J	F	M	A	M	J
J	A	S	O	N	D

Sole
Solea solea

ID FACT FILE

SIZE:
To 60 cm long

DESCRIPTION:
Body flat, rather long and narrow, tapering off gradually towards the tail end. Eyes on the right. Colouring on eyed side from medium to dark brown, with darker blotches. Tail small. Short 'whiskers' beneath head

HABITAT:
In rock pools

LOOKALIKES:
Other flatfish, of which this is the most narrow-bodied species found on shore

The largest specimens of this species are found in deeper waters offshore, and only smaller juvenile individuals are usually found in rock pools in the intertidal zone. Here it is most likely to be present in large pools with sandy bottoms into which the sole can 'disappear' with a rapid vibration of its body, leaving only the eyes visible. Spawning takes place in spring and early summer in shallow water just offshore. This is a widespread fish in northern European waters, southwards to the Mediterranean.

FISH

| J | F | M | A | M | J |
| J | A | S | O | N | D |

Topknot
Zeugopterus punctatus

ID FACT FILE

SIZE:
Up to 25 cm long

DESCRIPTION:
Body flat, almost
rectangular in
outline with a
large head and
bulging eyes
which are
positioned on the
left side of the
head. Body rough
to the feel.
Colouring on
eyed side from
dark to light
brown, with a
rounded dark
brown blotch in
the middle of the
upperside

HABITAT:
Rock pools

LOOKALIKES:
Several other
flatfish, but none
on shore has
almost
rectangular
outline

The Topknot is probably the most handsome of
all the flatfish and generally lives offshore in
depths of 1–25 m. However, it can also
sometimes be seen swimming around in rock
pools at low tide, or may be spotted lurking
imperceptibly on the gravelly bottom of a pool.
It can also cling quite firmly to the underside
of rocks and stones where these make a
smooth fit for the body whose entire
undersurface functions as an adhesive disc.
The Topknot occurs widely around the coasts
of northern Europe, but tends to be rather
local, although it may crop up quite regularly
in certain favoured localities.

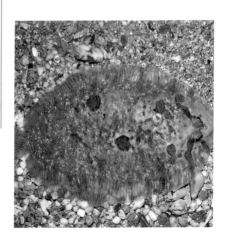

FISH

J	F	M	A	M	J
J	A	S	O	N	D

Shore Clingfish
Lepadogaster lepadogaster

ID FACT FILE

Size:
To 8 cm long

DESCRIPTION:
Body flattened
from top to
bottom but very
broad just behind
the head when
viewed from
above,reddish-
orange, with
scattered brown
markings and
two conspicuous
blue spots on
top behind the
head. Dorsal and
anal fins joined
to tail

HABITAT:
Lower shore,
under rocks or
seaweeds

SEASON:
May–October,
migrates
offshore in winter

LOOKALIKES:
Connemara
Clingfish, *L.
candollei*, has
anal fin separate
from tail fin and
red spots on
head of males

This fish is often found clinging to the
underside of a stone, using a powerful sucker
disc that is situated on the underside, behind
the head. If picked up it can be difficult to put
down again, as the sucker adheres to human
skin just as well as to rock. It can change colour
quite rapidly to match its background, for
example from pinkish-orange to almost black.
Masses of golden eggs are laid beneath stones
and guarded by either of the parents.
Distribution is from the western coasts of the
British Isles and western Channel southwards
to the Mediterranean.

BIRDS

J	F	M	A	M	J
J	A	S	O	N	D

Shag
Phalacrocorax aristotelis

ID FACT FILE

SIZE:
To 76 cm long

DESCRIPTION:
Plumage
blackish-green,
oily-looking. Bill
yellow, bill and
head quite small
in relation to
body. Neck quite
long, thin and
flexible. Legs
and feet black,
feet webbed

HABITAT:
Nests on rocky
cliffs

SEASON:
Breeds March–
September

LOOKALIKES:
Cormorant, *P.
carbo* has white
chin (plus white
nape and neck in
continental form)

The very widespread Shag is almost exclusively found on the sea coast, unlike the Cormorant, which is found on the coast, but is also common on fresh water inland. In summer the basic black of the Shag's plumage is overlain by an attractive greenish sheen, more conspicuous from some angles than others. The feathers on top of the head can be raised as a crest. In the breeding season large colonies form on steep cliff faces, the nest being a rather untidy mass of sticks and dried seaweed.

BIRDS

J	F	M	A	M	J
J	A	S	O	N	D

Eider
Somateria mollisima

ID FACT FILE

SIZE:
To 58 cm long

DESCRIPTION:
Drake with
diagnostic white
back and black
belly. Crown of
head also black,
side of head
white, beak
yellowish, rather
narrowly
triangular in
profile. Female
uniformly brown
with black
mottling

HABITAT:
Nests on flat
seashores

SEASON:
Breeds
April–June

LOOKALIKES:
Drake none; in
female King
Eider, *Somateria
spectabilis*
difficult to
distinguish

In winter this duck can turn up just about anywhere on the coasts of northern Europe, when its distinctive mode of flying – short bouts of active wing beats alternating with bouts of gliding – will give it away even at a distance. In summer it breeds in the north of its range e.g. in northern England and Scotland but not further south in the British Isles. Nesting takes place in flat, open, well-vegetated areas on islands and the tops of beaches. The female (illustrated below) lines her nest with a mass of soft down from her breast.

BIRDS

J	F	M	A	J
J	A	S	O	N	D

Herring Gull
Larus argentatus

ID FACT FILE

SIZE:
To 56 cm long

DESCRIPTION:
Head and body white, top of wings grey, tipped with black. Beak yellow, with red spot near its tip. Legs and webbed feet flesh-pink (yellow in eastern Europe and Mediterranean)

HABITAT:
Nests on coasts; forages everywhere

SEASON:
All year; breeds April–August

LOOKALIKES:
Common Gull, *L. canus* smaller (to 50 cm), with greenish bill lacking a red spot

Herring Gulls are common everywhere inland as well as on every coast, foraging on rubbish tips and following the plough in large numbers. This is also the gull that is most likely to come and sit near you waiting for a handout when you stop for a sandwich break on a cliff-top walk or have a snack on the beach. They become very tame and in well-visited seaside tourist spots you have to walk round them. This gives you a chance to get a close view of the red spot on the beak, at which the chick aims its peck to induce the returning adult to serve up a meal.

BIRDS

Lesser Black-backed Gull

Larus fuscus

J	F	M	A	M	J
J	A	S	O	N	D

ID FACT FILE

SIZE:
To 53 cm

DESCRIPTION:
Head and body white, top of wings slate black, with white on tips. Bill yellow with red spot. Legs and webbed feet yellow. Tail white

HABITAT:
Everywhere, but less common inland than Herring Gull

SEASON:
All year; breeds May–August

LOOKALIKES:
Great Black-backed Gull, *L. marinus* is larger (to 67 cm), with pinkish legs, a heavier, darker yellow bill and blacker shade on wings

Although becoming quite bold in well-visited spots, this is never quite as tame as the Herring Gull, *L. argentatus*, see opposite, and generally maintains a rather greater distance from humans. It is found everywhere on the coasts of Europe but is not quite as common as the Herring Gull inland. The adults form large nesting colonies on islands, isolated beaches and on moorland inland. The eggs are placed in a simple scrape in the ground, which the adult will defend valiantly. Its raucous, bugle-like call is very much a part of the seaside experience.

J	F	M	A	M	J
J	A	S	O	N	D

Common Tern
Sterna hirundo

Terns are smaller, more streamlined and far more graceful than gulls, and with their long, forked tails are sometimes called 'sea swallows'. The Common Tern forms large, bustling and very noisy nesting colonies on sandy islands, beach tops, and marshy areas near the coast and inland. The adults will often sit tight on the nest until a human comes just a little too close, when you risk having the top of your head attacked with a sharp bill as you are dive-bombed by the tern, quite unafraid in the defence of its nest. Mixed colonies of this widespread European species are often formed with the Arctic Tern, a more northerly breeder.

ID FACT FILE

SIZE:
To 36 cm long

DESCRIPTION:
Body sleek and elegant, white, with long forked tail. Top of head and nape black. Legs red all year round. Bill red with a black tip. Wings narrow and pointed, silvery grey on top with darker tips

HABITAT:
Nesting on shingle beaches or flying at sea

SEASON:
Summer visitor; breeds April–July

LOOKALIKES:
In the Arctic Tern, *S. paradisaea*, bill is all-red. Sandwich Tern, *S. sandvicensis* bigger, with black beak having a yellow tip

BIRDS

J	F	M	A	M	J
J	A	S	O	N	D

ID FACT FILE

SIZE:
To 42 cm long

DESCRIPTION:
A tall, upright bird with a long, narrow black bill, fairly slender neck, brownish-black head and back and white underparts. Legs and webbed feet black

HABITAT:
Breeds on cliffs and rock stacks

SEASON:
All year; breeds May–July

LOOKALIKES:
Razorbill, *Alca torda* has thicker neck, deeper almost square-topped head and deeper, flatter-sided bill

Guillemot
Uria aalge

The Guillemot is found all round the coasts of northern Europe wherever the cliffs are rocky and steep enough to provide nesting sites that cannot be reached by predators lacking wings. Guillemots are a common enough sight in such places during the summer months, but are rarely seen in winter, which they spend far out at sea. Due to lack of suitable breeding habitat along the extensive low stretches of the southeast coast of Britain, Guillemots are also rather rare in this area.

INDEX